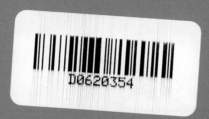

FAMILY TRIVIA

BRAIN-TEASING PUZZLES & CAPTIVATING GAMES

This edition published by Parragon Books Ltd in 2017

Parragon Books Ltd
Chartist House
15–17 Trim Street
Bath BA1 1HA, UK
www.parragon.com

ISBN 978-1-4748-6916-4

Printed in China

Images courtesy of iStock and Shutterstock

FAMILY TRIVIA

BRAIN-TEASING PUZZLES & CAPTIVATING GAMES

250 ENGROSSING ACTIVITIES & TESTING INTERACTIONS TO VEX & PERPLEX

Parragon

Bath • New York • Cologne • Melbourne • Delhi
Hong Kong • Shenzhen • Singapore

INTRODUCTION

Puzzles, tricks and games are an integral part of any culture, encompassing all age groups and suiting both solo puzzlers or groups of people spending leisure time together.

If you like to challenge yourself with a puzzle or have fun with friends and family, with a bit of fierce competition thrown in, then *Brain-Teasing Puzzles & Captivating Games* will give you a range of stimulating options. It's certainly true that nothing beats a bit of mental stimulation. By doing a puzzle, playing a few games, or demonstrating a few conjuring tricks and illusions you can get people bonded, talking, laughing and relaxing together.

Did you know what has to be broken before you can use it? Or what walks on four legs in the morning, two legs at midday and three legs in the evening? Or how many times you can subtract 10 from 100? Or how to cut a length of string in half and then make it whole again?

Including a collection of conundrums, problems, teasers and mental hurdles to keep you thinking clearly, along with a selection of traditional family games and tricks, here is an assortment of diversions to keep both the fun and the focus in your life.

USING THIS BOOK

The puzzles, tricks and games are interspersed throughout the book, with each one simply identified by the icons below:

Puzzle

Game

Trick

The puzzles and riddles have not been graded to indicate the degree of difficulty, as different puzzlers will find different kinds of puzzles either easy or hard. Some people are adept at number-based puzzles; others are better at word problems. Most of the puzzles and riddles require some lateral thinking, meaning that the obvious route to the answer is not always the correct one, but all can be tackled by puzzlers of any age.

The selection of games includes tried and trusted, traditional family pastimes, but there are also some that have been given a modern twist to keep younger participants interested and older players on their toes! Tricks can require some preparation but mostly involve using only items that can generally be found around the house.

The puzzle solutions can be found at the back of the book (from pages 210–224), and each puzzle has a note giving the page number where the solution can be found.

For young children, games and tricks marked with this symbol will require adult assistance or supervision due to the inclusion of sharp or small objects, or the use of glue.

01. STRANGE OBJECT

I am not strong, yet the strongest door cannot stand in my way. I am not rich, yet I can access things of great value. I have no friends, yet people will stand in the street to wait for me.

WHAT AM I?

Solution on page 210

02. WEIGHTY PROBLEM

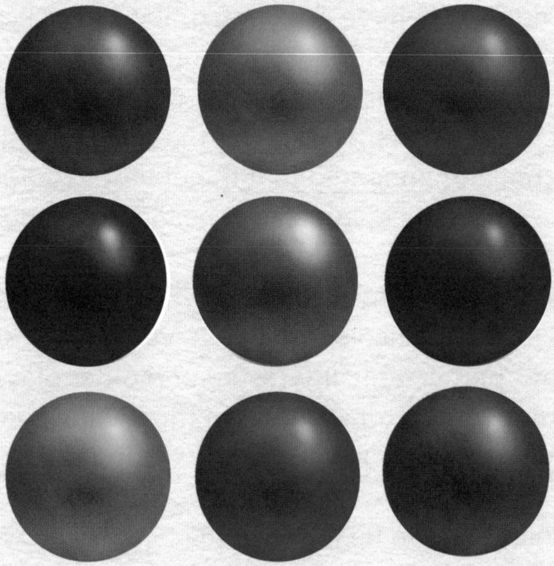

You are handed a bag containing nine balls that are identical in size but one is slightly heavier than the others. How many times do you have to load a balance scales in order to find out which is the heavy ball?

Solution on page 210

03. LIMERICK TAG

2+ players
Take it in turns to make up a silly limerick, one line at a time.

WHAT YOU WILL NEED:

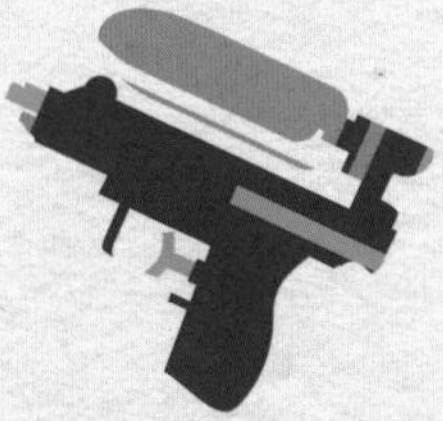

- A stopwatch

WHAT YOU MUST DO:

Everyone has to make up a line of a limerick to add to the line that has gone before. If there are lots of you, you can split into teams to work together on your lines.

A limerick is a poem with five lines and always scans the same way, such as:

A girl soaked her father with water
From a squirter that he had bought her
She laughed like mad
Until she saw Dad
Had a squirter for soaking his daughter!

One player or team is chosen to start and the next player has 30 seconds to come up with the next line. You can make the rhyme as silly as you like but if you can't come up with something, you are out of that round and have a penalty point marked against you. The others then carry on.

The player who finishes the limerick then has to start a new one and the player or team at the end of the limerick session with the fewest penalty points is the winner.

04. CUP CONUNDRUM

How can you put ten counters into three cups so that each cup contains an odd number of counters?

Solution on page 210

05. CHECK MATE

Two friends play chess once a week. Last week they played five games. Each won as many games as the other, but no games ended in a draw, and no games were left unfinished.

HOW CAN THIS BE?

Solution on page 210

06. LABEL MIX-UP

Harry has three boxes of fruit on his market stall. He has one box containing only apples, one box containing only pears, and one box with a mixture of apples and pears. There is a label on each box describing the contents but none of the labels is on the correct box.

HOW CAN HARRY WORK OUT WHAT IS IN EACH BOX BY TAKING JUST ONE PIECE OF FRUIT FROM ONE BOX?

Solution on page 210

07. FIVE FINALISTS

Five friends have a race. Alan finished after Simon. Ian finished after Kevin. Simon finished after Brian. Kevin finished before Alan. Brian finished after Kevin. Brian finished before Alan. Simon finished before Ian. Alan finished before Ian.

WHO FINISHED WHERE?

Solution on page 210

08. TRA (ART BACKWARDS)

2+ players

The object of this game is really simple. All you have to do is to draw a picture of something suggested by one of the other players – a house, a cow, a car or a flower, perhaps – but you must not look at the paper. You can do your drawing only by looking in a mirror.

WHAT YOU WILL NEED:

- A mirror
- A pen or pencil
- Paper for drawing on
- A book or magazine to lean on

WHAT YOU MUST DO:

Each player must take a turn at creating a drawing. If you have a small mirror that can stand on a table or be propped up against a wall, that is ideal. Lay your sheet of paper down so that you can see it in the mirror and then draw your picture without looking directly at the paper – it's a lot more difficult than it sounds! If you have a large wall mirror, you can use it to play the game with each player taking it in turns to stand in front of the mirror holding the drawing paper against their body. You will need to use a book or magazine under the paper to play the game this way.

The results are usually hilarious and will probably be the worst, shakiest and most scribbly sketches you have ever done, so don't be upset if everyone else laughs at your drawings. The whole point of this game is for everyone to have a good laugh.

09. SNAP!

2+ players
This is an easy card game but you have to keep your wits about you because it can move very fast. You can play with more than eight players, but it then becomes a bit too spread out and it can be difficult to see exactly what is happening.

WHAT YOU WILL NEED:

- A pack of cards

WHAT YOU MUST DO:

All of the players sit around a table and the dealer deals the cards face down, one to each player, until all the cards have been dealt. The cards remain face down, but players must sort their own into a neat stack.

The player to the left of the dealer starts. He takes the top card from his stack and places it down face up so that everyone can see it, starting a new stack. The next player then takes the top card from his stack and places it down to start his own face-up stack. Everyone must do the same, in turn, watching as a new card is turned over.

If a player turns over a new card that matches the top card on any other player's face-up stack, the first player to shout 'Snap!' wins all of the cards from the face-up stacks of the one who has just played, and the one who has the matching card. The dealer judges who was first to shout. Matching cards have to be of the same rank – a two of hearts matches a two of spades, clubs or diamonds; a queen of clubs matches a queen of hearts, diamonds or spades.

The game continues until one player has won all of the cards. If you run out of cards to turn over but still have some in your face-up stack, you stay in the game waiting to spot a 'Snap!' and win some cards to carry on.

10. GLASS TEASER

WHAT YOU MUST DO:

Six glasses are standing in a row.

The first three have water in them, but the second three are empty.

How can you make the row of glasses alternate between full and empty when you are only allowed to touch or move one glass?

Solution on page 210

11. HAPPY FAMILIES

Mr and Mrs Smith have six daughters.
If each daughter has one brother,

HOW MANY CHILDREN ARE IN THE FAMILY?

Solution on page 210

12. LESS IS MORE

The more you have, the longer you'll live; but the more you have had, the less you have left.

WHAT ARE THEY?

Solution on page 210

13. CHARADES

4+ players

Charades is a great game that can be played by large groups that include players of all ages. It gives everyone a chance to show off their acting skills, although the acting has to be done as a mime because the player is not allowed to speak.

WHAT YOU MUST DO:

If you are the first player to take a turn, you must think of the title of a book, movie, play, TV show or song. You then have to stand in front of all of the others and mime clues for them to guess the title.

To begin with, the player has to let everyone know in which category their chosen title belongs. For this part, there are accepted mimes.

For a book, you press your hands together, palms inward, and then open them up as though you are opening a book.

For a movie, you hold your left fist up to your eye (some use the nose) as though you have a movie camera in front of your face, and circle your right fist in the air at the side as though you are turning the crank on an ancient movie camera.

For a play, you hold your arms together in front of you and then sweep them up to the sides as though they are stage curtains.

For a TV show, you hold your two forefingers together in front of you, then move them apart, down and back together to trace the shape of a TV screen in the air.

For a song, you hold your mouth open and throw your hands out from your chest like an opera singer.

The others will shout out 'Movie!' if it's a movie and you point to the first one to shout and put your other index finger on your nose to indicate that they are correct.

Now you have to hold up the number of fingers that corresponds to the number of words in your title. If your title is *The Empire Strikes Back*, then you hold up four fingers to indicate four words. Someone will call out 'Four words!' and you point and touch your nose to show they are correct. We can use this title to demonstrate some of the mime techniques you are allowed to use. Remember that you are not allowed to speak, mouth words or make noises, but you can point at objects in the room if that helps.

The others will shout out guesses during your mime, so it is important that you point to someone who guesses part of your title correctly and touch your nose. That way everyone knows how the guessing is going.

There are some accepted ways of miming certain words. If it is a small word, like 'the', you hold your thumb and forefinger close together to show everyone a small space. People will guess 'But', 'An' or 'It' but someone will eventually say 'The'. Point and touch your nose.

'Empire' is a tricky word to mime, so hold up three fingers to show that you are going for the third word. You can then mime hitting something, or even swinging a baseball bat for 'strike'. People will shout 'bash', 'hit' and so on, but someone will get 'strike'. Point and touch your nose, then use your sign for a small word but widen the gap to show that the word you are looking for is bigger than 'strike' and they will guess 'strikes'.

Hold up four fingers to show you are doing the fourth word. Point to your back. Once they've guessed 'back', they will be pondering over 'The (something) Strikes Back...'

Hold up two fingers to show you are doing the second word. Tap the two fingers on your forearm to show that the word has two syllables (em-pire). Hold up two fingers again and place them on your forearm to show you are giving them the second syllable. Give your earlobe a tug. This is the sign for 'sounds like' and you can use it for a syllable, a whole word or an entire title. You could try miming warming your hands by a fire, which sounds a bit like 'pire' and from that your audience would have 'The Fire Strikes Back'. Surely they would then guess the title?

The person who guesses first is the next person up to take their turn miming a title in front of everyone and you can now relax and take part in the guessing.

14. STAYING DRY

Solution on page 211

Ten people are meeting at a restaurant, walking from three different directions. Only one of them has an umbrella, but they all arrive at the same time and none of them gets wet.

HOW DID THEY MANAGE IT?

15. TOPSY TURVY

How do you turn this shape upside down by moving only two lines?

Solution on page 211

16. FIND THE COIN

2+ players
Find the chosen coin using the power of your mind.

WHAT YOU WILL NEED:

- Ten coins of the same value so that they are exactly the same size
- A cloth or plastic bag
- A blindfold
- A marker pen

WHAT YOU MUST DO:

Put all of the coins into the bag and then ask a volunteer to choose one. Your volunteer must then use the marker pen to write his or her initials on the coin.

When the ink is dry, ask the volunteer to hold the coin very tight in his or her hand and to concentrate very hard on the coin. After a minute, the volunteer drops the coin into the bag and you give the bag a shake to mix them up.

The volunteer can then blindfold you after which you reach into the bag and rifle through the coins. Say that you are trying to pick up the mental energy that the volunteer's concentration transferred to the coin. Then pull out the coin with the volunteer's initials on it.

HOW DID YOU DO IT?

You felt around in the bag for the coin that was warm from being held tightly in the volunteer's hand.

17. CENTURY

2+ players
Keeping track of your score requires a bit of arithmetic – and that helps to sharpen your wits!

WHAT YOU WILL NEED:

- Two dice
- Pencil and paper

WHAT YOU MUST DO:

Players take it in turns to throw the dice and add up their score each time they throw.

They throw both dice at once and have only one throw per turn.

If they score a double, that score counts as double, so two fives will count as 20, and not 10.

Each player keeps his or her own score on a piece of paper and the first one to reach 100 is the winner.

18. NEW BALLS PLEASE!

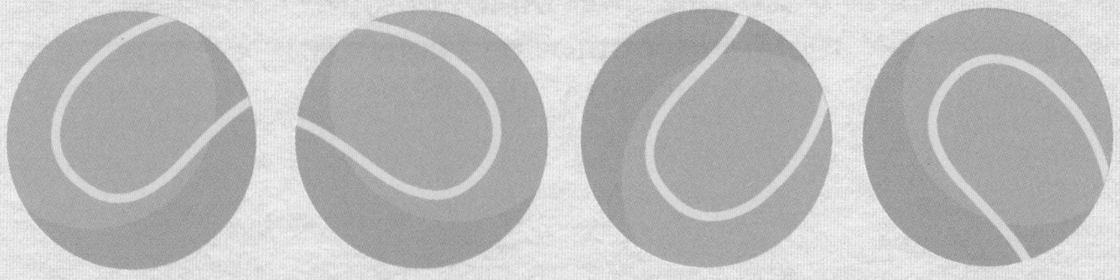

A boy and a girl are both carrying baskets of tennis balls. The girl says to the boy, 'If I give you one of my tennis balls, we will have the same. But if you give me one of yours, I will have twice as many as you.'

HOW MANY DID EACH HAVE?

Solution on page 211

19. ON TOP OF THE WORLD

Mount Everest, the highest mountain in the world, was conquered in 1953 by New Zealander Sir Edmund Hillary and Nepalese Sherpa Tenzing Norgay.

WHAT WAS THE HIGHEST MOUNTAIN IN THE WORLD BEFORE MOUNT EVEREST WAS DISCOVERED?

HINT
You don't have to be a professor of history to consider what was different about the world before 1953.

Solution on page 211

20. LADDER JUMPER

How can you jump off a 10-metre (35-foot) ladder onto solid concrete and not hurt yourself?

Solution on page 211

21. THE SOCK DRAWER

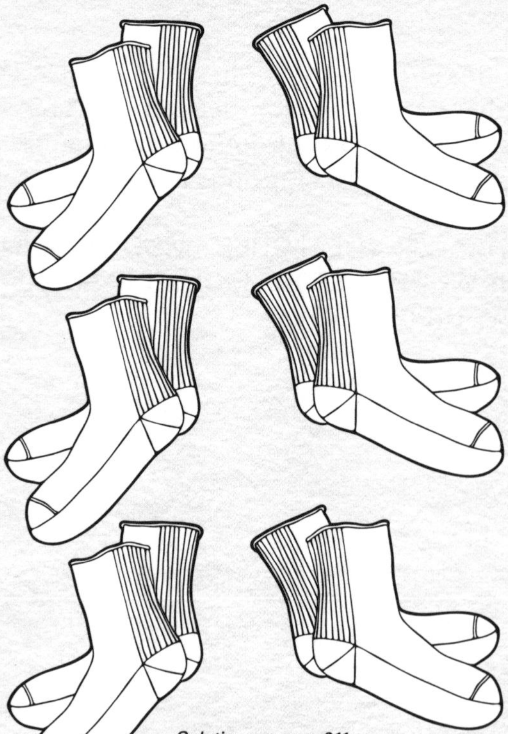

You have 10 black socks and 12 white socks in a drawer but they are all jumbled up, none of them together in pairs. How many times do you have to reach into the drawer and pull out a sock, without looking,

TO END UP WITH TWO MATCHING SOCKS?

Solution on page 211

22. WORDS AND PICTURES

3+ players
Use your imagination to create bizarre pictures and captions.

WHAT YOU WILL NEED:

- A sheet of paper for everyone
- A pencil for everyone

WHAT YOU MUST DO:

The whole point of this game is to create the silliest pictures and captions that you can dream up so that everyone can have a good laugh at the end result.

Everyone starts with a sheet of paper. At the top, write a caption like, 'The dog's tail wagged round and round when it saw its food bowl.'

Everyone then passes their paper to the person sitting on their right. Now you all have a paper with someone else's caption at the top. Your task now is to draw a picture beneath the caption, showing what you think is going on in the caption.

Next, fold the paper over at the top to hide the caption and pass the paper to your right. Everyone now has a drawing in front of them. Add a caption below it. The player with the dog and bowl might think it is 'Helicopter hound meets alien ship.'

The top of the paper must now be folded over again so that the drawing is now hidden and the paper passed on to the right with only the new caption showing. This time everyone must draw something to go with that caption.

Keep going like that – writing, drawing, writing, drawing – until the paper is full. Then you can unfold the paper in front of you and read out the strangest illustrated story ever, holding it up so that everyone can see the weird drawings. There are no winners and losers – it's all just to make each other laugh!

23. MOVIE TREATS

James, Dominic and Sarah are watching a movie together and sharing some chocolates. James can eat 27 chocolates in one hour. Sarah can eat 2 chocolates in 10 minutes. Dominic can eat 7 chocolates in 20 minutes.

HOW LONG WILL IT TAKE THEM TO EAT THE WHOLE BOX OF 120 CHOCOLATES?

Solution on page 211

24. MATTER OF TASTE

What will always taste better than it smells?

Solution on page 211

25. ELEPHANT

2+ players
The last one to turn into an elephant is the loser!

WHAT YOU WILL NEED:

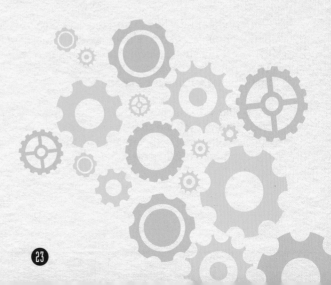

- A pack of cards
- A piece of paper
- A pencil

WHAT YOU MUST DO:

Select a set of four cards for each player – four eights, four queens and so forth – then put all of the other cards aside.

The dealer now draws an elephant and puts it in the middle of the table. He or she then shuffles the selected cards and deals each player four.

The players look at their cards. The aim is to end up with four matching cards. If no one immediately has a set of four, then the dealer calls 'Pass' and everyone takes one card from their hand and passes it to their left.

This continues until someone gets a set of four. If you do, you say nothing, you just put your thumb on your nose with your little finger pointing outwards to make an elephant's trunk. Quick as they can, everyone does the same and the last to make a trunk takes the elephant from the middle.

The one who takes the elephant, keeps the card until the next round when someone else may win it by being last.

26. THE LOST CARD

2+ players
Amaze your friends when you have them 'lose' a card that they have chosen from a deck and you find it without having known what the card was.

WHAT YOU WILL NEED:

- A deck of cards

WHAT YOU MUST DO:

A little preparation is required for this trick and it has to be done before you present the trick so that no one sees you doing it. You have to remove all of the spades from the deck and put them in order, counting the ace as '1' and the king as '13'. Return the spades to the deck at the bottom with the ace at the very bottom. Your deck of cards, standing face down, will now have the ace of spades facing the table and above it will be 2, 3, 4, 5, up to king of spades with the rest of the pack stacked above the king.

Hold the deck out towards a willing volunteer and ask him or her to choose a card. You have to make sure that they do not disturb the bottom 13 cards in the deck, so grip the deck near the bottom with your thumb and forefinger to protect the spades you have put there.

Your volunteer can look at the card, but must not show you. Ask the volunteer to cut the deck, taking half the deck off the top and setting it aside face down. The volunteer must then put the chosen card on top of the pile set aside and place the other pile on top. The chosen card is now hidden in the middle of the deck, but because you know that the ace to king of spades were originally on the bottom of the deck, the ace is now sitting on top of the chosen card.

The volunteer now has to turn the deck face up and cut the deck, which will reveal a new card on top of the remaining pile. If this card is not a spade, tell the volunteer to complete the cut by placing the remaining pile on top of the new pile, still face up. They must then cut again until a spade is revealed. Do not let your volunteer know that you are looking for a spade.

If the spade that is revealed is, for example, the five, it means that the four, three, two, ace and then the chosen card are now on the bottom of the pile just set aside. The volunteer can complete the cut, then ask him or her to turn the deck over so that the cards are now face down.

You know that the top card on the deck is now the four of spades. Ask your volunteer to start taking cards from the top of the deck one at a time without turning them over. Without seeing what they are, he or she will take the four of spades, then the three, then the two, then the ace, then the chosen card. Stop the volunteer, ask him or her to turn over that card and then say, 'This is the card that you chose!'

Obviously, at the stage when the deck is being cut face up, if the nine of spades appears, the chosen card will end up as the ninth from the top; if it is the jack of spades it will be the eleventh, and so on.

1.

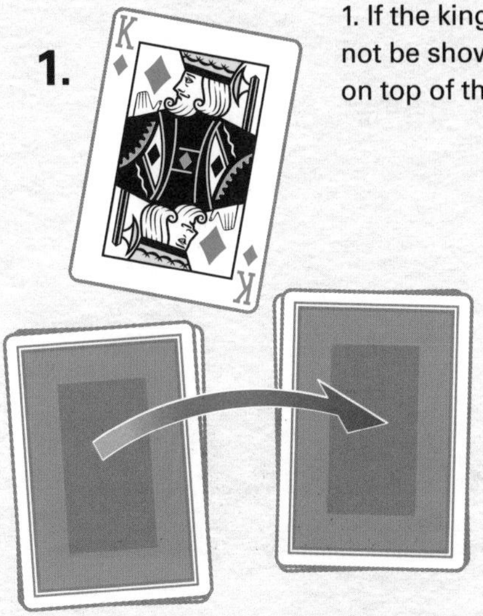

1. If the king of diamonds is chosen, you will not be shown it and it will be placed face down on top of the right-hand side of the cut deck.

2.

2. The deck is turned over for the face-up cuts. Each cut must be completed and a new one started until a spade appears.

3.

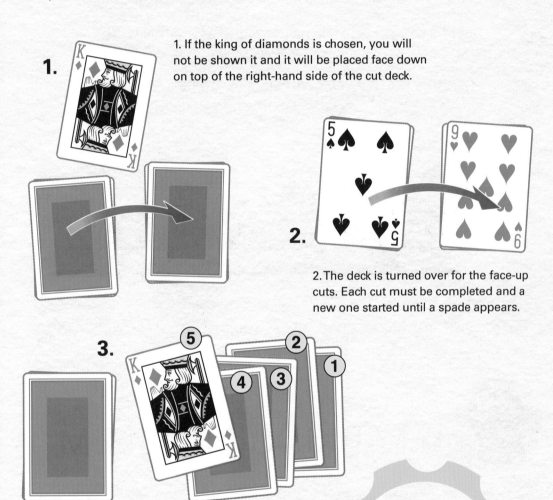

3. If a five of spades has appeared, you know that the king will be the fifth card from the top of the pile when the deck is turned over again.

TIP

Be sure to let your volunteer do all of the cutting so that you do not have to touch the cards and the trick will seem even more amazing.

27. READY TO RACE

Forty rally cars line up at the start of a race.

5 per cent of the cars carry one spare wheel.

Out of the 95 per cent left, half carry two spare wheels and half have no spare at all.

HOW MANY SPARE WHEELS ARE THERE IN TOTAL?

Solution on page 211

28. PARKING PROBLEM

How many cars can you park in an empty garage?

Solution on page 211

29. FENCE ME IN

2+ players
No ordinary dot-to-dot, you have to think quickly to win at this game.

WHAT YOU WILL NEED:

- A large sheet of paper
- A pencil

WHAT YOU MUST DO:

Mark out a grid of dots on the paper. A grid that is ten dots by ten dots should make for a good game.The players each take turns to draw one horizontal or vertical line on the grid joining two dots that are side-by-side. If the line that you draw closes off fences in a square, you write your initials in the square and take another go.

Once there are lots of lines on the grid, it may be that one player is able to fence in a square, take another turn, fence in another square and keep going several times.

The player with most squares when the grid is full is the winner.

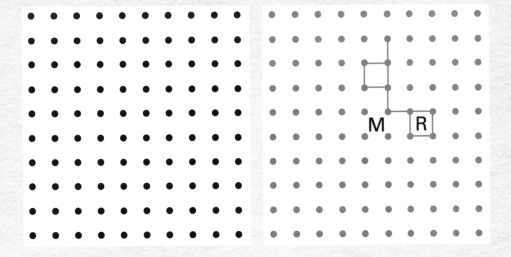

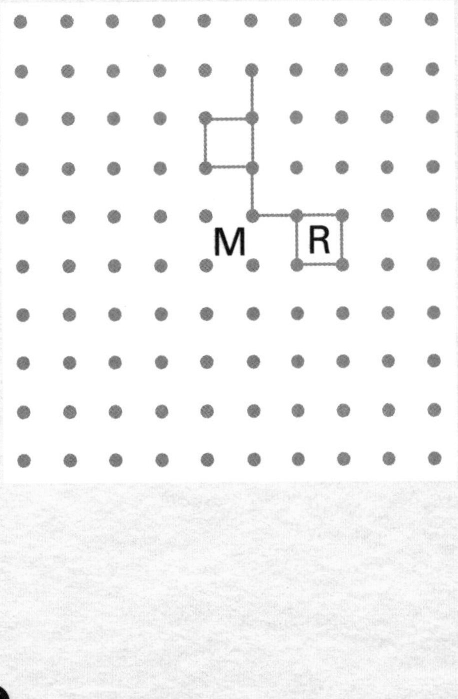

30. SHELF SNACK

A three-part encyclopedia is sitting on a bookshelf. There are 300 pages in each part. A bookworm chews its way from the first page of Vol 1 to the last page of Vol 3.

Not counting covers, how many pages has it burrowed through?

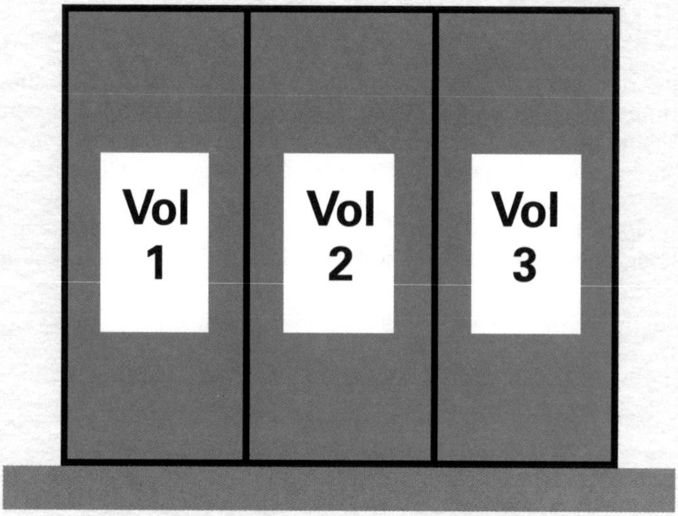

HINT
Think about the way the books sit on the shelf and where the hungry bookworm starts munching its way through them.

Solution on page 211

31. CHATTERBOX

2+ players
Anyone who loves to chatter on about nothing in particular will become a grand champion at this game in just 30 seconds!

WHAT YOU WILL NEED:

- A stopwatch
- A bowl, hat or bag
- A piece of paper and a pencil for each player (or at least enough pencils to share)

WHAT YOU MUST DO:

Each player writes a topic on a piece of paper and the papers are all put into the bowl or hat. The first player then picks out a topic. The object of the game is to talk about the topic for 30 seconds non-stop without repeating words (you can repeat words like 'the' or 'and' but not words that are important to the topic), without stumbling over your words or pausing, and without talking about things that have nothing to do with the topic.

The players must all choose the umpire, who will be in charge of timing and decide if there has been repetition or any other rule breaking by the speaker. The other players can shout 'Object' if they think there has been a pause, repeated words or the speaker has gone off-topic, but the final word goes to the umpire. The umpire will stop the clock while the objection is discussed, and must decide whether to accept it or overrule it.

If accepted, the player who made the objection must take over the topic, speaking for whatever time is left. If rejected, the original player takes up the story again and must try to keep talking until the 30 seconds are up.

The umpire can award points to players for successful objections or successfully completed topics. Once the first topic is exhausted, a new player chooses a paper from the hat.

TIP
When you are talking, don't get yourself confused by trying to talk about history or technical things. Stick to your own personal opinions on the topic to avoid coming unstuck!

32. CAVE DWELLER BOULDERS

2+ players
You need space to create a bowling alley for this game, and you'll have to build a cave to bowl your boulders into.

WHAT YOU WILL NEED:

- A cardboard box – a shoe box is ideal
- A pair of scissors
- A pen
- Some marbles

WHAT YOU MUST DO:

The first thing that you must do is create your cave. Take the lid off the cardboard box or cut off the top. It needs to be turned upside down on the floor so that it can sit with its 'walls' directly on the floor. You now have to cut a series of entrances to your cave. These doors can be arches, or triangles, or thin slots. When your cave is on the ground you will be trying to get marbles (your boulders) in through these openings.

Use the pen to mark a score above the openings. If it is a narrow opening, give it a high score of ten. If it is a wide opening and easier to aim for, give it a low score of two or three.

Each player, or cave dweller, then takes it in turns to roll a boulder at the cave. You win points for getting your boulder inside. If you miss and your boulder is sitting outside the cave, or you score and it rolls back out, you must leave it there. Another cave dweller may knock it in and can claim the points. The one with most points when everyone has used all their boulders is the winner.

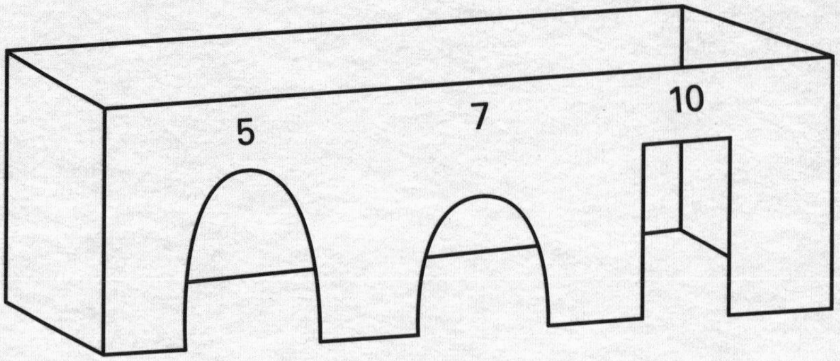

33. IT'S BEHIND YOU!

4+ players
Be the first to find out what animal is sneaking up behind your back!

WHAT YOU WILL NEED:

- Paper and pencils for all players
- Sticky tape

WHAT YOU MUST DO:

Each player has to draw an animal, a bird or a fish on their piece of paper. It's probably a good idea to write the name of the animal as well, just in case the drawing isn't too recognizable.

The players must not let any other players see what they are drawing. The drawings are all then handed to a referee who keeps them safe while all of the players line up. The referee then uses the sticky tape to attach a drawing, at random, to the back of each player.

The players can't see what animal is behind them and they must all stand in a circle facing each other. Players take it in turns to turn round, show everyone their animal, turn back and ask one question, such as 'Does it have feathers?' or 'Can you ride on its back?' The other players must answer truthfully but can only call out 'yes' or 'no'.

When one player's question has been answered, the next player shows their animal. When a player has asked enough questions to guess what animal is sneaking up behind him, on his next turn he can ask the question, 'Is it an eagle?' or 'Is it a camel?' If he's right, he sits down and the rest carry on until everyone has guessed correctly.

34. MYSTERY OBJECT

I am made of solid wood but if
I drop on your foot, it won't hurt.
You can stand on me and I will
not break. You can pick me up
quite easily, but I cannot be
cut with a saw.

WHAT AM I?

Solution on page 211

35. GIVE AND TAKE

Taking me for yourself can be brave
but giving me to someone to whom
I do not belong is wrong.

WHAT AM I?

Solution on page 212

36. TWIN TROUBLE

Two girls are born to the same mother at the same time, on the same day, in the same year, yet they are not twins.

WHY IS THIS?

Solution on page 212

37. FRUITY PROBLEM

A teacher, Miss Turner, has 11 children in her class. In a bowl on her desk there are 11 apples. Miss Turner divides the apples among the class so that each of her pupils has a whole apple, but there is one left in the bowl.

HOW CAN SHE DO THIS?

Solution on page 212

38. LESS IS MORE

The more of these you take, the more you leave behind.

WHAT ARE THEY?

Solution on page 212

39. IN THE HOLE

How much soil is in a round hole with a circumference of 10 metres (35 feet) and a depth of 10 metres (35 feet)?

HINT
Think about the work you have to do to dig a hole and what that work involves, no matter how big the hole might be.

Solution on page 212

40. FISHING FOR ICE CUBES

2+ players
How can you use a thread to fish an ice cube out of a glass of water without touching the glass, the water or the ice cube?

WHAT YOU WILL NEED:

- A glass
- A thread
- Some cold water
- Some salt
- An ice cube

WHAT YOU MUST DO:

First you have to drop an ice cube – preferably a fresh ice cube straight from the freezer – into a glass of cold water. Now you can challenge everyone to try to get the ice cube out of the glass using a strand of thread and without touching the ice, the water or the glass.

Seems impossible? You can't tie a thread around an ice cube without touching the water, after all, can you? In fact, you don't need to.

The trick is simply to lay the thread across the top of the ice cube and then sprinkle a little salt over the ice. The salt will dissolve the surface of the ice cube but it will re-freeze almost straight away, and the thread will be frozen to the surface.

You can then lift the ice cube out of the water, dangling from the end of the thread that is frozen to it.

Ensure that you do not allow the salted ice cube to touch your skin, and allow the cube to dissolve in the glass before pouring the water away.

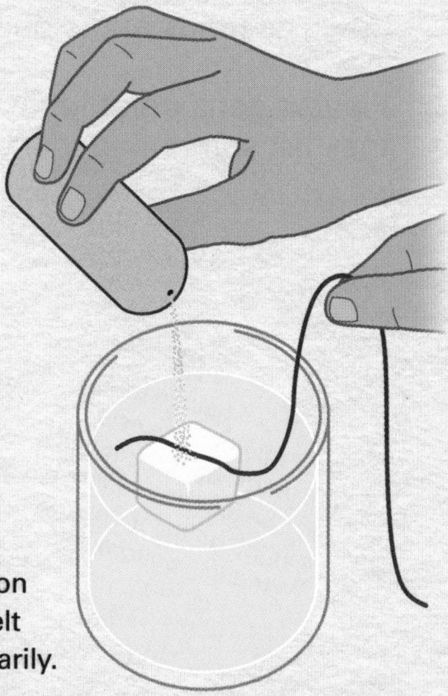

Pouring a little salt on the ice cube will melt its surface momentarily.

41. KIM'S GAME

2+ players
When the character, Kim, was being trained as a spy in Rudyard Kipling's 1901 novel *Kim*, this game was used to improve his ability to remember lots of details.

WHAT YOU WILL NEED:

- A tea tray
- A cloth big enough to cover the tray
- 15 to 20 objects
- A stopwatch
- Paper and pencils

WHAT YOU MUST DO:

This game needs a Memory Master who must be in charge and set up the game.

The Memory Master has to arrange at least 15, but not more than 20, objects on a tray and write down what each one is. The Memory Master then covers the objects with the cloth and places the tray in the middle of a table where everyone can see it.

The Memory Master uncovers the objects, giving everyone exactly one minute to study the tray and remember what is there. When time is up, the tray is covered again and the players have two minutes to write down as many of the objects as they can remember.

Players get a point for every object they remember but lose a point if they list something that was not actually there.

Then, while everyone turns away, the Memory Master removes one item from the tray and calls for everyone to turn round again. The first player to spot what is missing gets five points. The one with the most points is the winner.

TIP
It can help to try to remember objects in patterns on the tray, such as 'the four in a square top right' or 'the three in a triangle bottom left.'

42. SPOTS BEFORE YOUR EYES

Take a look at the nine spots shown on this page. Your challenge is to connect all of the spots using just four straight lines, and to make things even more difficult, you have to do it without lifting your pen from the paper.

Solution on page 212

43. FAMILY TIES

Sharon is John's daughter.

This means that John is the __________ of Sharon's father.

Solution on page 212

44. CRISS CROSS

What is the maximum number of Xs you can draw on this noughts and crosses board without making three in a row in any direction?

Solution on page 212

45. AROUND THE WORLD

Imagine that you could lay a piece of string on the ground that stretched right around the world. The circumference of the Earth is about 40,000 km (25,000 miles). You must assume that your piece of string is lying on a flat surface all the way round. Now imagine that you have an army of people standing on your piece of string. They are holding a second piece of string and each of them is holding it exactly one metre (3.3 feet) above the ground. This second piece of string, therefore, circles the Earth one metre (3.3 feet) above the surface. How much longer must the second piece of string be?

HINT

If you have looked at the radius of a circle during school lessons, then you should be able to work out that the second piece of string needn't be as long as you might first expect.

Solution on page 212

46. DISAPPEARING MONEY

2+ players
There's a twist to this magic trick in that your money doesn't want to disappear and stays right where you left it!

WHAT YOU WILL NEED:

- A light cloth such as a tea towel
- An orange (or an apple)
- A coin

WHAT YOU MUST DO:

Tell your audience that you are going to make a coin disappear off the table in front of you, but try to appear a little uncertain about the trick and let them know that you have had problems with it before – this is all part of your act.

Place the coin on the table in front of you and slide it around a bit as you are talking to your audience. Tell them that you are going to cover the coin with the cloth, but admit that they then won't be able to see where the coin is. You are sliding the coin to let them get used to the sound of the coin on the table – but don't tell them that.

So that they can see where the coin is at all times, place the orange on top of the coin. Now cover both with the cloth and pinch the cloth in around the bottom of the orange by making a frame of your forefingers and thumbs.

Move the cloth around on the table and the audience will hear that the coin is still there. Ask them to concentrate hard on helping you to make the coin disappear and move the cloth towards you, away from you and from side to side. They can still hear the coin, so obviously the trick hasn't worked yet.

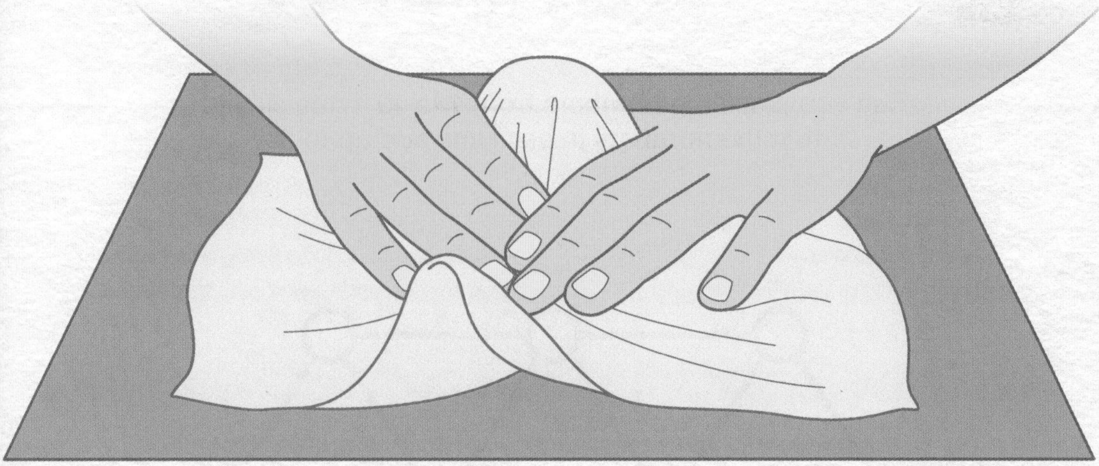

Gather the cloth around the orange and support it so that it will keep its shape when you secretly drop the orange into your lap.

Try again, pulling the cloth towards you with your hands always maintaining the frame around the orange. Everyone can still hear the coin.

Now you must appear to lose your temper a bit and quickly whack the cloth-covered orange with your hand. It flattens. You remove the cloth and the coin is still there, but the orange has disappeared!

The trick is to move your thumbs apart for a moment when you pull the cloth towards you the last time. You have to let the orange roll off the coin, off the edge of the table and into your lap, all under the cover of the cloth. By keeping your forefingers in place, you can keep the round, orange-shaped bulge in the cloth, so everyone thinks the orange is still there. They can hear the coin, after all, so they think that both are still under the cloth when you flatten it.

TIP

Practice makes perfect. Practise moving the orange around under the cloth and practise dropping it into your lap, chatting all the time to distract your audience.

47. THE GREAT 38

Can you place the numbers from 1 to 19 in the circles so that the numbers in each line add up to 38?

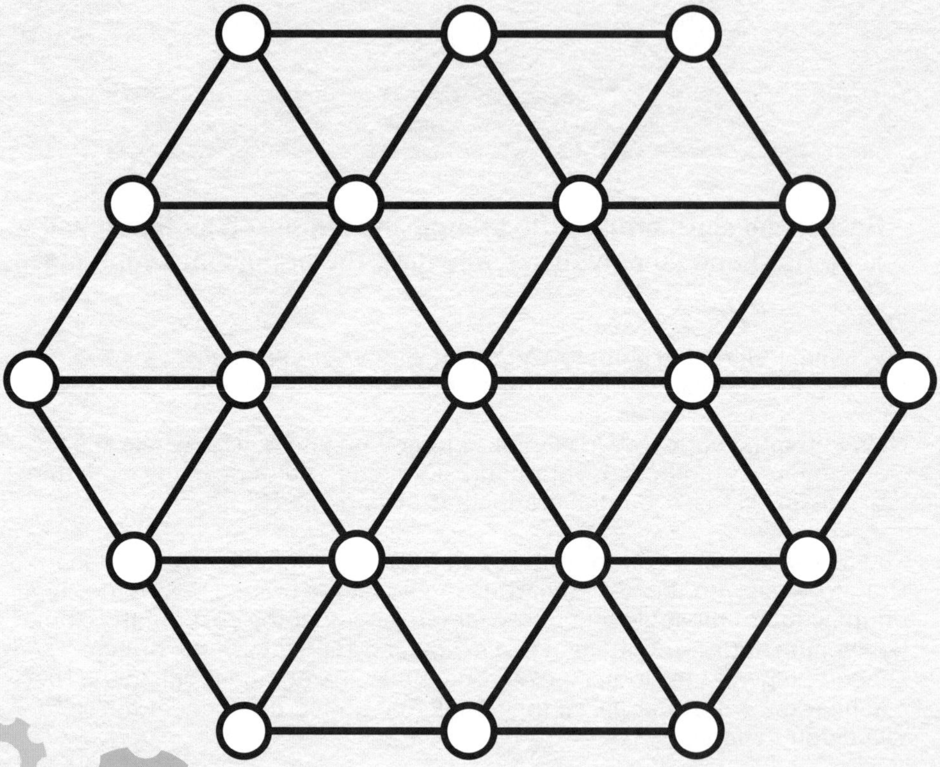

Solution on page 213

48. DOODLE MONSTER

2+ players
Use your creative talents to turn a scribble into a creature as fabulous as your imagination can conjure.

WHAT YOU WILL NEED:

- Coloured pencils
- Paper
- A stopwatch

WHAT YOU MUST DO:

Each of the players sitting round a table draws a squiggle on a piece of paper and passes it on to the player sitting to the right.

The players then have ten minutes to turn the squiggle into the most fantastic monster that they can think of. It can be part animal, part robot or lots of parts of different animals – anything goes.

After ten minutes the players can all have a good laugh at each other's drawings as they explain, in turn, what their creature is, where it lives and what it eats. They can then vote for the scariest, weirdest and funniest efforts.

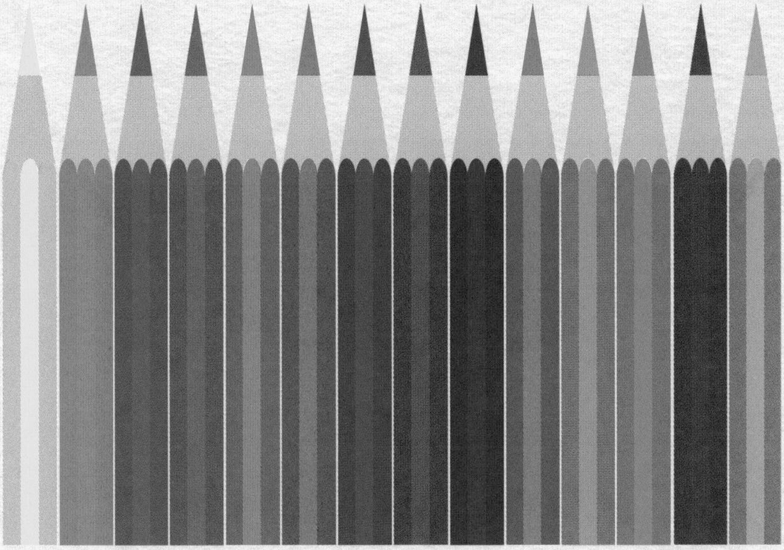

49. ANGRY SHEEP

A farmer has ten very bad-tempered sheep that he keeps in a circular paddock. The sheep cause a bit of a problem when they start fighting with each other, so he has to separate them. He has three circular fences that he can use to keep them apart. The fences can intersect each other, but how does he arrange the fences so that each of his ten sheep is fenced off from all of the others?

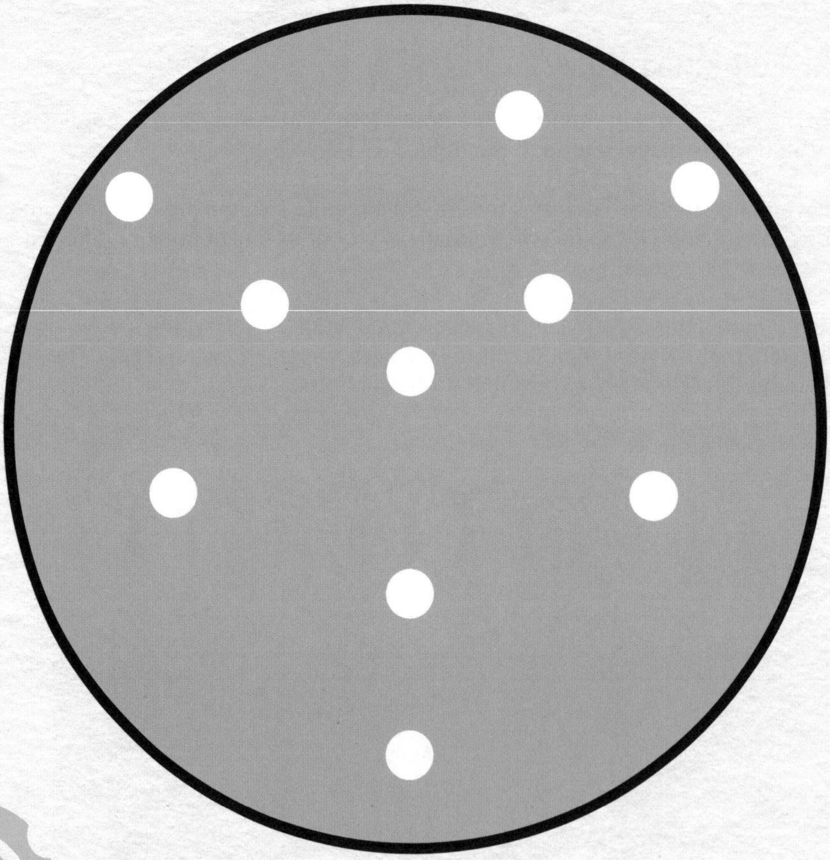

Solution on page 213

50. PICK-UP STICKS

2+ players
This is a race with a difference because you are aiming to be last!

WHAT YOU WILL NEED:

- As many toothpicks as you can lay your hands on (at least 25)

WHAT YOU MUST DO:

Lay out the toothpicks neatly in columns and rows so that they all line up like soldiers on a parade ground. You should try to have as many columns as you do rows, so if you lay out a first row of five toothpicks, you will need another four rows beneath it. You can have ten or more columns and rows, depending on how many toothpicks you have, but you should have at least five (diagram 1).

The players take it in turns to pick up toothpicks. You can pick up as many as you like from a column or row as long as they are next to each other with no gaps created by missing toothpicks that have already been picked up.

The first player might pick up the entire second row, for example (diagram 2). The second player can then pick up the whole of rows 1, 3 or 4 but only either the first toothpick in one of the columns or from the third toothpick to the end of any column.

The aim, remember, is to be last to pick up, so thinking ahead and leaving gaps that stop your opponent from picking up everything that remains is the key to winning.

DIAGRAM 1

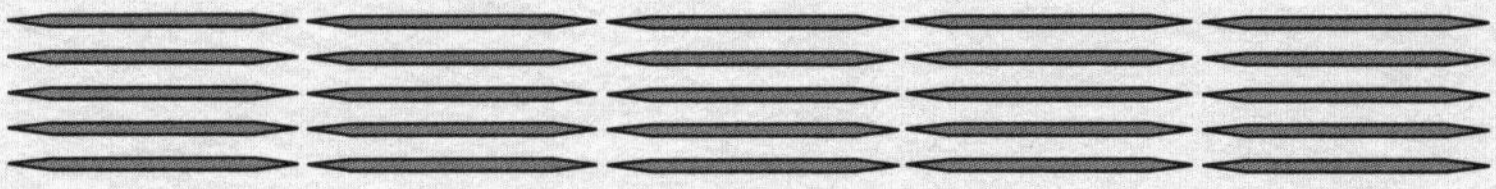

DIAGRAM 2

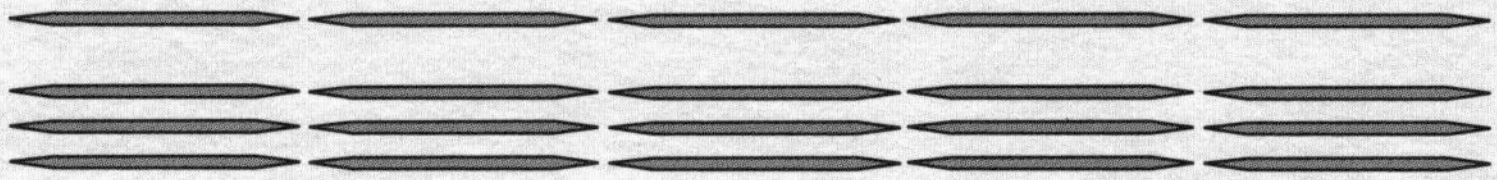

51. SQUAWK OF TRUTH

A young man was invited to a party in the palace of an Arabian prince and there he met the most beautiful girl he had ever seen. From the moment he was introduced to her, he was in love. As they strolled through the palace gardens they heard a voice saying, 'You look lovely!'

They turned to see a brightly coloured parrot perched on the branch of a tree. The young woman thought that the talking parrot, with its fantastic plumage and cheeky speaking voice, was simply wonderful.

The next day the young man went to the great bazaar in town, determined to buy a parrot like the one at the palace. It was to be a gift for the young woman, to help him win her heart. He found a merchant who had for sale a parrot almost identical to the one in the prince's palace. When he asked if the parrot could talk, the merchant promised him, 'This parrot will repeat every word it hears.' The young man immediately bought the parrot and spent the next few days trying to teach the bird to say, 'I love you', but the parrot uttered not a single word. The young man took the parrot back to the bazaar and complained to the merchant that the bird would not talk, yet the merchant claimed he was being completely truthful when he said that the bird would repeat every word it heard.

HOW COULD HE HAVE BEEN TELLING THE TRUTH?

HINT

Being able to talk is not always as valuable a skill as being able to listen.

Solution on page 213

52. THE NAME GAME

David's mother
had three children.

The first child was named April;
the second child was called May.

What was the third child called?

Solution on page 213

53. CREATE 100

Using the same number between
1 and 9 and any of these
mathematical symbols
(÷, +, −, ×),
create a calculation
that equals 100.

Solution on page 213

54. FLAPPY FISH RACING

3+ players
Flappy Fish Racing is a lot of fun but, if you aren't too keen on fish, then don't worry. Real fish are not required but you do need real jockeys. Each player is a fish jockey, racing his or her own fish. If you are in charge, you must be the starter and also judge who has won at the end of the race.

WHAT YOU WILL NEED:

- An old newspaper
- A pair of scissors
- A marker pen
- A selection of magazines
- A pencil

WHAT YOU MUST DO:

Use the marker to draw a fish shape on the newspaper. Make it nice and fat and at least 30 cm (1 foot) long.

Cut out the fish, but cut through several layers of the newspaper at once, so that you have several identical fish.

Each of the jockeys then writes his or her name on a fish.

Lay the fish flat on the floor along a starting line with their heads pointing towards a finishing line on the other side of the room.

Each jockey is given a magazine and put under starter's orders.

The starter calls 'Paddle!' and the jockeys flap their magazines, slapping them on the floor to create a draughtt and blow their fish towards the finishing line.

The fish may get mixed up when they flap off in all directions, but the first to cross the line wins, no matter which jockey gave it the final flap.

TIP
You will need lots of floor space for Flappy Fish Racing, but it can get a bit crowded with too many jockeys. Run separate, smaller races, then the winners can compete in a grand final.

55. THE INTERROGATOR

3+ players

The whole point of this game is to answer The Interrogator's questions without cracking a smile, but keeping a straight face is not as easy as you might think. Normally, you have to think of an answer when you are asked a question, but in this game you already know the answer – it's the question that takes you by surprise!

WHAT YOU MUST DO:

At the start of the game, all of the players have to agree on a phrase that will be the answer to The Interrogator's questions, no matter what the questions are. The sillier you make the phrase, the better, and everyone must answer the questions using the same phrase. Let's say you make the phrase 'A kangaroo wearing a pirate's hat.'

One player must now take the first turn at being The Interrogator. His or her job is to make you smile or giggle when you give your answer, and The Interrogator can ask anything at all. The Interrogator's first question might be, 'What did you have for breakfast?' You must answer, 'A kangaroo wearing a pirate's hat.'

If you answer without smiling or giggling, then The Interrogator moves on to the next player and makes up another question, such as, 'What does your maths teacher look like?' or 'Who goes to work on a unicycle?' or 'What do you see when you look in a mirror?'

Smile or titter and you're out, but you then become the new Interrogator and you can decide whether a new answer phrase has to be devised.

56. KETCHUP MIND CONTROL

3+ players
We all love ketchup, right? Well, almost all of us – but nobody likes messing around with those fiddly little sachets. Even if you can find the easy way to open one, you know you're going to end up with ketchup dribbling between your fingers or splashing your shirt.
So how much more would you love ketchup if you could control one of those sachets using only the power of your mind?

That's the sort of introduction that you need to give your audience before you go on to amaze them by demonstrating ketchup mind control. You will make an intact, unopened sachet of ketchup rise, fall and even hover inside a sealed plastic bottle full of water. There's no way you can physically touch it, yet you will be able to make it move.

WHAT YOU WILL NEED:

- One large, clear plastic bottle with a screw top and any labels removed so that you can see straight through it.
- One unopened sachet of ketchup.

WHAT YOU MUST DO:

Fill the bottle with water and fold or scrunch the sachet a bit in order to push it lengthwise into the bottle, so that it sits in the water the right way up. A little water will be displaced and spill out, but don't worry about that.

Screw the lid back on the bottle. The ketchup will be floating near the top of the bottle. Talk to your audience, tell them what you are doing and encourage them to concentrate on the ketchup.

Now grip the bottle in one hand, with your fingers towards the audience and your thumb on your side of the bottle. Your fingers will obviously hide part of the bottle, but everyone will still be able to see the ketchup moving at your command.

Next, use your free hand to wave at the ketchup and call out 'Down! Down! Down!' Make sure that everyone else is concentrating and joining in. The trick is then secretly to squeeze the bottle slightly, without letting the audience see you do it. A gentle squeeze will make the ketchup sachet sink to the bottom.

Command the sachet to 'Rise! Rise! Rise!' and relax your squeezing hand, again without letting the audience see you doing it. The sachet will float upwards inside

the bottle. With a bit of practice, you should be able to judge your squeeze so that you can make the ketchup 'hover' halfway up the bottle but remember to grip the bottle with your fingers towards the audience.

If you hold the bottle to one side, they will be able to spot your secret squeeze. Always remember to keep talking and make lots of movements with your free hand to disguise the fact that you are squeezing the bottle.

1. Let your audience see the sachet going into the bottle.

2. Turn your hand to give the audience this view ...

3. ... then they won't be able to spot you giving the bottle a gentle squeeze.

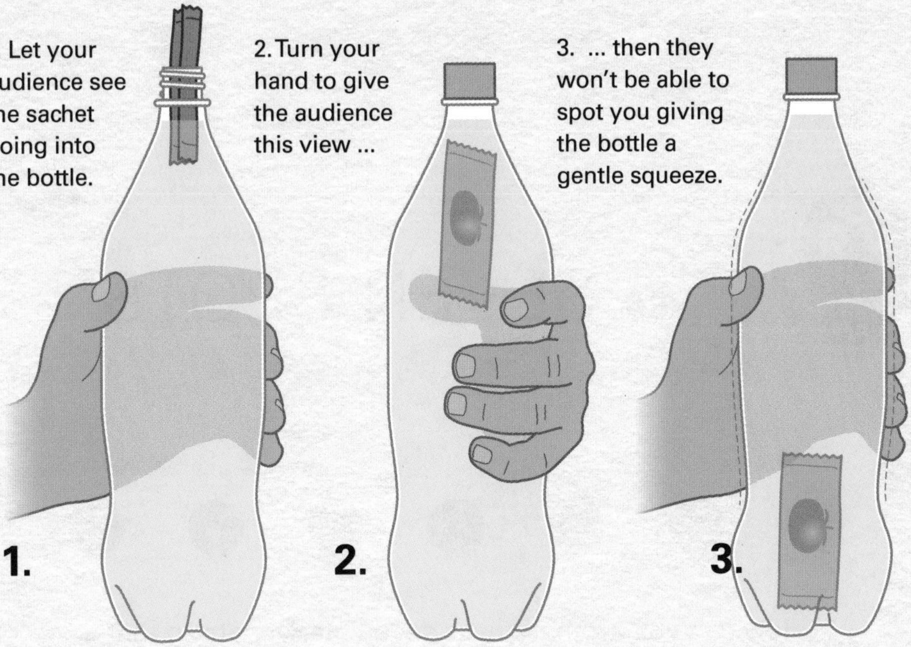

TIP

Tell your audience you need their mind power to help you, and get them to join in when you say 'Down!' or 'Rise!' That makes it more fun and helps you to disguise your secret squeeze.

57. BUTTERFINGERS

If you drop me I am sure to crack,
but smile at me and I will smile back.

WHAT AM I?

Solution on page 213

58. SEVEN SPOTS

How can you arrange these seven black spots so that there are six rows with three spots in each row?

HINT
Equal rows don't always mean a square grid.

Solution on page 213

59. TRIANGLE OF TEN

Reverse this triangle of ten counters by moving three.

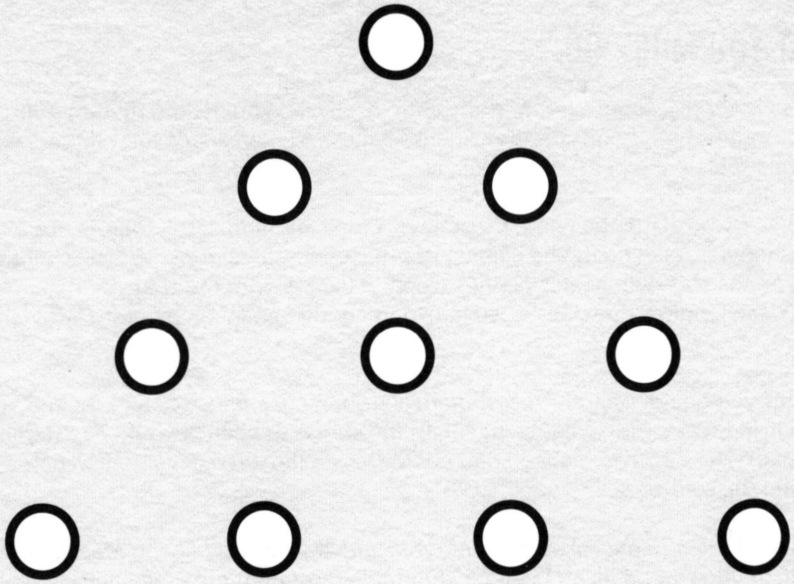

Solution on page 214

60. SLAP-CLAP-SNAP!

3+ players
This game is all about being able to concentrate, keep to a rhythm and think quickly. Once the game is underway, a little distraction or someone getting the giggles can be enough for you to lose the beat and crash out of the game.

WHAT YOU MUST DO:

The idea is simple. Once everyone is sitting in a circle, you get the rhythm going. Everyone slaps both hands on their knees, claps, and then snaps their fingers left and right. This sets up the beat – slap, clap, snap, snap – 1,2,3,4.

The person who starts the game must have a topic in mind. If the topic is, for example, famous movies, then he or she chants, 'Names-of, fam-ous, mov-ies.' The chanting comes on the slap-clap beats: 'Names(slap)–of (clap)', with the snap-snap giving two beats pause before 'Fam(slap)–ous(clap)' and another snap-snap before 'Mov(slap)–ies(clap).'

That gets you going. After 'Mov-ies' there is a snap-snap pause before the next player in the circle gives a movie name, again on the slap-clap beat. It could be 'Star(slap)–Wars(clap)'. There is then a snap-snap pause before the next player has to name a movie on the slap-clap.

Obviously, longer names like *Those Magnificent Men in Their Flying Machines* are tricky to fit into two beats and you have to rattle through them really quickly. Hearing you deliver a tongue twister can give the next player the giggles, causing him or her to mess up their answer. That player is then out of the game.

A player is out if he or she loses the beat, gives a wrong answer or gives an answer that has already been used – repeats are not allowed.

When a player is out, the next player begins again with a new topic – maybe sports cars, rock stars or wild animals. Once the players have each named two or three 'in-sects', it becomes quite difficult to think of another in time to deliver it without losing the beat.

61. GONE IN A MOMENT

As soon as you talk about me, I am gone. Even saying my name will always make me disappear, and you can say nothing to make me return.

WHAT AM I?

Solution on page 214

62. HIGH JUMP

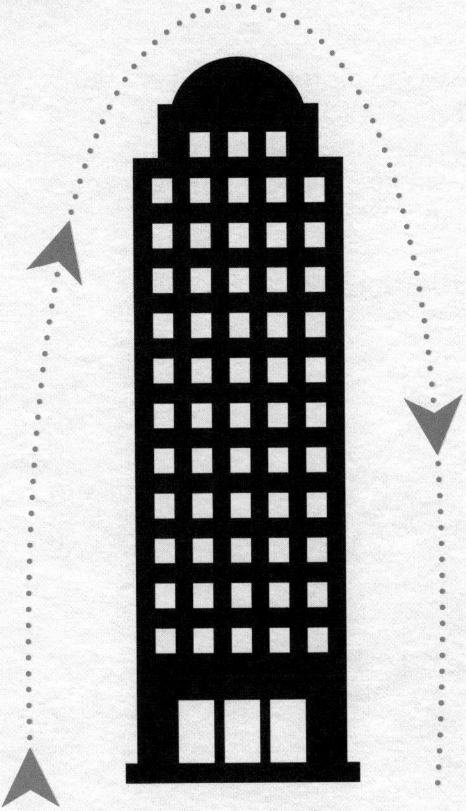

What creature can jump higher than a building?

HINT
It's not how high the creature can jump that makes the real difference here!

Solution on page 214

63. STRANGE GUESTS

They arrive in the evening without invitation
and leave in the morning without saying goodbye.

WHO ARE THESE STRANGE GUESTS?

Solution on page 214

64. GIANT PROBLEM

Two tribes of giants have been at war for many years but decide to have a peace conference. Each tribe sends 20 of its tallest giants to the conference. Because they are giants, they like to be tallest and will only shake hands with others who are smaller than themselves.

HOW MANY SHAKE HANDS?

Solution on page 214

65. PANTS ON FIRE

5+ players
Ideally, you should have at least six players for this game, split into two or more teams of three, but you can make it work with five.

WHAT YOU WILL NEED:

- A dictionary
- Pad of paper
- A pen
- A stopwatch

WHAT YOU MUST DO:

The first team has three minutes to look up an unusual word in the dictionary. They write the word down on a piece of paper. One player memorizes the true meaning of the word, the other two have to make up daft definitions that are totally false.

The word is then revealed to the other team or teams and each of the players in the first team presents their definition in turn, giving a detailed explanation to persuade the opposition that they are telling the truth.

Once the others have made up their minds, they call on each of the first team to sum up their definition. As each states his or her answer, the opposition calls out 'Liar, liar, pants on fire!' if they think the player is telling a big fat fib, or 'True, true, it's you!'

The first team must then reveal who was telling the truth. The opposition gets a point if they guessed correctly, but nothing if they got it wrong. The dictionary is then passed to the next team.

66. TOUGH TRIANGLES

These two triangles are formed with six toothpicks in total.
The challenge is to use only the same six toothpicks to
form four triangles, all of an equal size.

Solution on page 214

67. PAIRS

2+ players
For some card games you need to learn complicated rules and know when best to make certain moves, but for this one all you need is a good memory.

WHAT YOU WILL NEED:

- A full deck of cards

WHAT YOU MUST DO:

Shuffle the cards thoroughly and then lay them out, face down, on a table in six neat rows with nine cards in each row – include the jokers. The game involves turning the cards over two at a time, so you need to leave a bit of space between the cards when you lay them out.

The first player has to turn over two cards. If the cards are matching – two kings, two fives or two tens, for example – the player keeps the two cards and has another go. If they do not match, the player turns the cards face down again, returning them to their original positions.

Everyone has to watch as the cards are turned over and try to remember where they are so that when it comes to their turn, if the first card they turn over is a four, they will know where to find another four.

There won't be many pairs to begin with, but as the game progresses, there will be more and more. The winner is the player who has the most cards when all of the pairs have been picked up.

Shuffle the pack well before you start a new game.

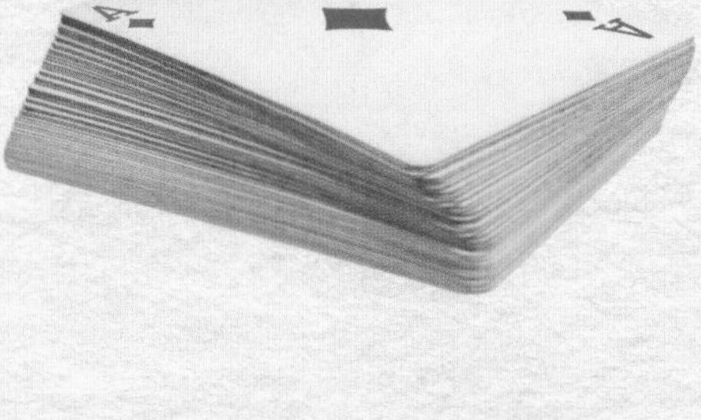

TIP
Look for easy ways to help you remember where cards are. If a five is the fifth card in a row or a three is in the third column, they are easier to remember.

68. PIRATE PUZZLE

Two pirate ships, one captained by Cutlass Jake and the other by Skeleton Pete, arrive at a desert island. Both pirate captains have identical treasure maps and they rush ashore to find the hidden loot. Eventually, they reach an ancient rock beneath which two treasure chests have been buried. One chest is half full of gold doubloons, while the other is half full of worthless lead discs that weigh the same as the gold.

They argue over the gold and both pirates and their crews have swords and pistols drawn, ready to fight.
They know that if a battle breaks out, none of them may survive, so Skeleton Pete suggests that he should divide the gold and the lead between the two chests. Cutlass Jake can then blindfold him and mix up the chests so that he does not know which is which. Pete will then pick one piece from one of the chests. If he chooses gold, he gets to keep all of the gold and his crew is rich. If he chooses lead, he gets the lead and Jake's crew takes all the gold.

How does Skeleton Pete divide the gold and the lead between the two chests to give himself the best chance of choosing gold?

HINT

Here's a clue that might help. Skeleton Pete has to divide the gold and the lead between the two chests, but he doesn't necessarily have to divide it evenly...

Solution on page 214

69. BEETLE

2+ players
You don't have to be a great artist for this game and there's no skill or strategy – it's all down to lucky numbers.

WHAT YOU WILL NEED:

- A die
- Paper and a pencil for each player

WHAT YOU MUST DO:

The object of the game is to draw a beetle that has a specific number of body parts. There is a body, six legs, a head, two feelers and two eyes.

Players take it in turn to roll the die. They must roll a 1 to get started. Rolling a 1 allows them to draw the body. Without the body, they can't add any of the other parts. It can take a few goes to roll a 1, but after that they need the following:

- A two for the head
- A three for each of the two eyes
- A four for each of the two feelers
- A five or a six for each of the six legs

The body must come first, but legs can be added to the body before the head. Similarly, you have to have a head on your beetle before you can add eyes and feelers.

The first one to finish their beetle is the winner.

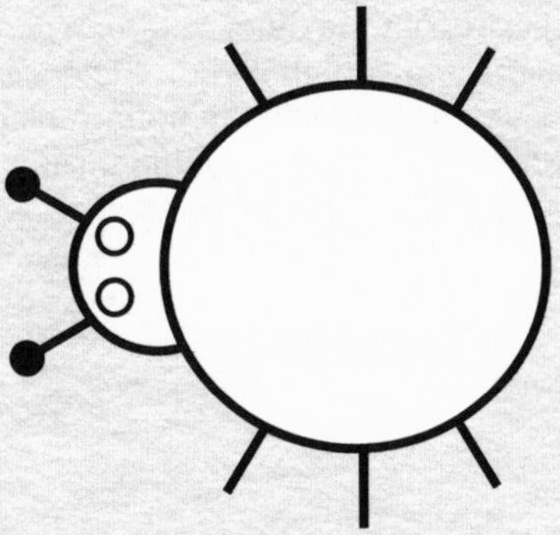

70. CUTTING THE LADY IN HALF

2+ players
Cutting the lady in half is a stage magician's trick but, with a little preparation, you can do it in your own living room.

WHAT YOU WILL NEED:

- A paper tube or envelope • A slip of paper
- A pencil • A pair of scissors

WHAT YOU MUST DO:

Draw your lady on the slip of paper. She is to be your beautiful assistant and you should announce her to the audience.

Now you need a paper tube or sleeve big enough for your assistant to fit inside. You can make a tube by sealing an envelope and cutting off the ends. You need to do this in advance so that you have your tube ready before you start doing the trick. This is because you need to make a couple of cuts in the tube. These need to be a little wider than your assistant because she needs to be able to fit through them.

Make the cuts across the back of your tube so that they will always be facing away from the audience. You will give the trick away if anyone sees these sneaky slots.

The idea is that you will put your paper assistant into the tube and then cut the whole lot in half, yet your assistant will emerge completely unscathed. The trick is to slip your assistant into the tube with the front of the tube facing the audience. They will not see that you are actually slipping your assistant out through the first slot at the back, and then back in through the second slot.

As far as the audience is concerned, they will see your assistant's head sticking out one end of the tube and her feet sticking out the other. You then use the scissors to begin cutting the envelope, always making sure that your audience only sees the front of the tube. At the back of the tube, you have to slip the bottom blade of your scissors between the tube and your assistant so that you are cutting through the tube but not the lovely lady.

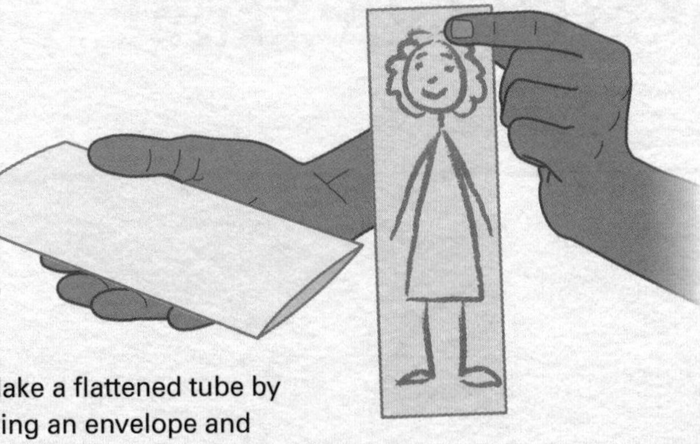

1.

1. Make a flattened tube by sealing an envelope and cutting off the ends. Draw your beautiful assistant on a piece of paper that will fit inside.

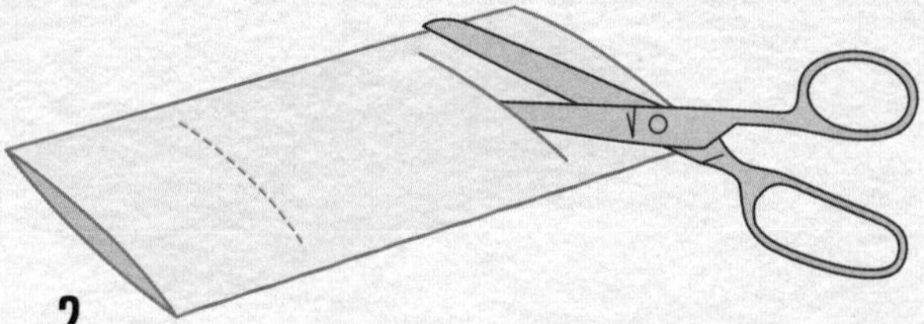

2.

2. Make two cuts in the back of the tube but do not let your audience see them.

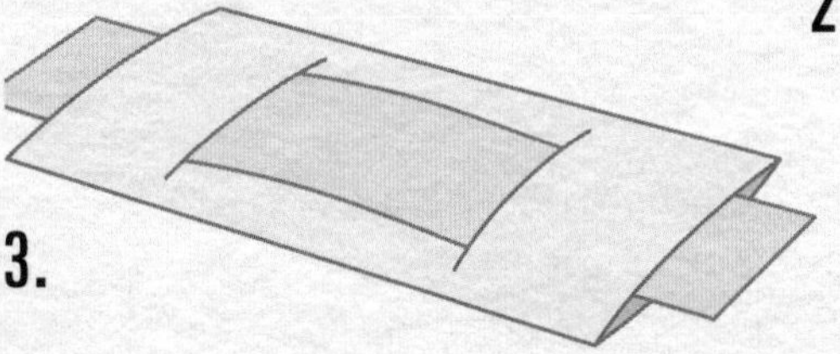

3.

3. When it looks like you are feeding your assistant into the tube, you actually send her out through the cuts and back in again.

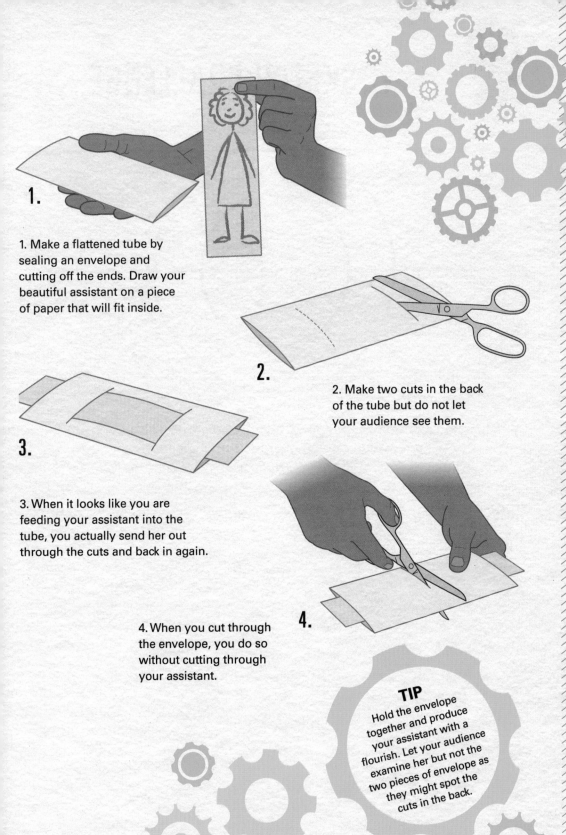

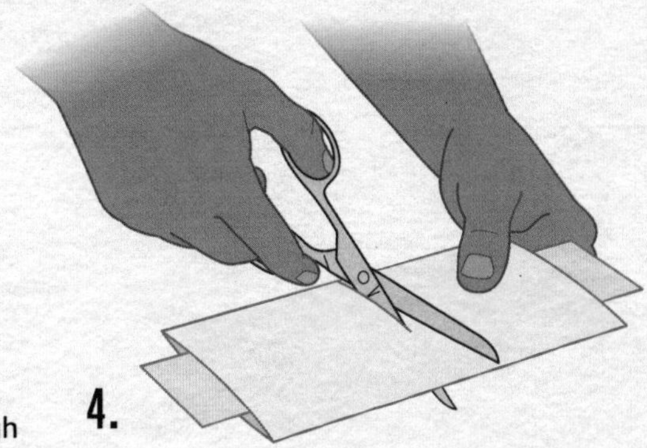

4.

4. When you cut through the envelope, you do so without cutting through your assistant.

TIP

Hold the envelope together and produce your assistant with a flourish. Let your audience examine her but not the two pieces of envelope as they might spot the cuts in the back.

71. SKETCH CHALLENGE

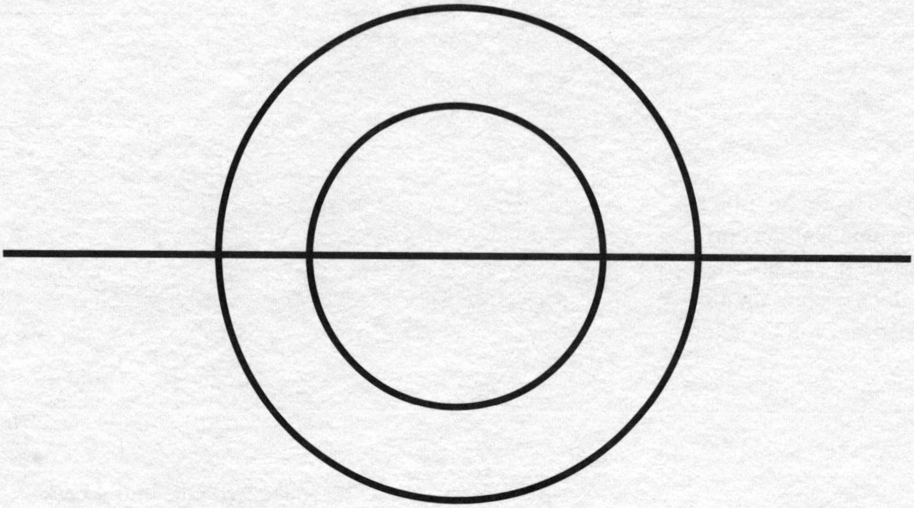

Can you recreate this shape without lifting your pen off the paper and without going over the same line twice?

Solution on page 214

72. HANGMAN

2+ players
This is a battle of wits where you have to work out the mystery word letter by letter, with every wrong guess taking you one step closer to losing.

WHAT YOU WILL NEED:

- Paper
- A pencil

WHAT YOU MUST DO:

The first player thinks of a word or phrase and marks it down on the paper as a series of dashes – one dash for each letter and a suitable space between words. The player gives one clue such as, 'It's a country' or 'It's a book title'.

The others now take it in turns to guess letters that may be in the mystery word. A player is allowed to guess just one letter. If the letter is correct, the first player fills in the blanks where the letter appears. If it is not, the first player can start his scaffold, adding one line to the drawing every time there is a wrong guess – first the base, then the upright, the supports, and so on.

With the scaffold complete, the head, body, arms, legs and feet of the man being hanged are added, one part for each wrong guess. The wrong letters are written down at the side so that everyone knows what has already been guessed. If the feet are in place before the mystery word is guessed, the first player has won the game and can choose whether to have another go or pass the paper to someone else.

73. STRETCH-A-SKETCH

2+ players
Even the world's greatest artists would struggle to create a decent sketch without being able to see what's further up the page.

WHAT YOU WILL NEED:

- A pencil
- Paper

WHAT YOU MUST DO:

The players sit around a table and the first player starts the sketch. You must all agree that you are drawing an animal, or an alien, or a soldier – something that starts off with a head, then has a body of some sort and ultimately legs and feet.

The first player starts with the head, and the last player knows that he or she will be finishing off with feet, or flippers, or whatever comes to mind. No one, however, is allowed to see what has gone before.

Taking care not to let anyone see what is being drawn, the first player sketches a head and then folds the paper back, so that the head is behind the blank paper with only a couple of little lines showing to let the next player know where to continue the sketch.

The second player folds the paper again, so that his or her contribution is also now behind the blank sheet and the next person carries on the drawing from the ends of the lines left by the second player. So it continues until the last person completes the drawing and the previous stages are folded back to reveal the most bizarre sketch imaginable!

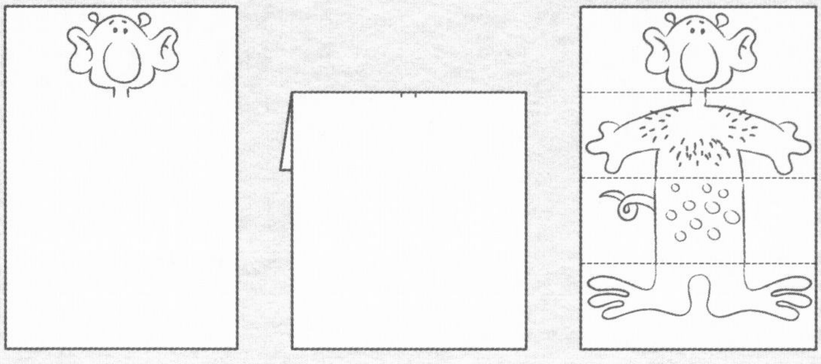

74. NOBODY'S SON

I am a father's child
and a mother's child,
yet I am no one's son.

WHY?

Solution on page 215

75. CAN YOU SEE?

The more there is of me,
the less you can see.

WHAT AM I?

Solution on page 215

76. PONTOON

2+ players
If you can count to 21, you are in with a chance in this game of luck and guesswork.

WHAT YOU WILL NEED:

• A pack of cards • Something to bet with such as tokens, beads or sweets. You can even cut up small squares of paper as tokens to make sure everyone has a dozen or so.

WHAT YOU MUST DO:

One person is nominated as the dealer. The dealer gives each player one card, placed face down in front of them. The dealer gives himself or herself a card last of all. Players look at their cards without letting anyone else see. The aim is to collect cards that will add up to 21, or as close as you can get. Picture cards count as 10 and an ace can be either 1 or 11. Players then place bets on whether they think they can get to 21. Minimum bet is one token, maximum is four, to be placed in the middle of the table.

The dealer then gives everyone a second card, face down. Players study their cards. A picture card, or a 10, and an ace would give 21 – pontoon – and any player who has a pontoon must say so. The dealer pays that player, and any other who has a pontoon, twice what he or she bet, unless the dealer also has a pontoon, in which case the dealer wins and takes everything that has been bet.

If no one has a pontoon, the dealer asks each player in turn if they would like another card and deals it face up. That card may take the player closer to 21 and they can ask for another card if they wish. If they go over 21, they are 'bust' and out of the game.

A player close to 21 can choose to 'stick' – take no more cards – and once everyone has either stuck or bust the dealer's cards are revealed. The dealer then chooses to take more cards or to stick. If the dealer gets closest to 21, the dealer wins. If the dealer goes bust, the player closest to 21 wins.

77. BUZZ

2+ players
You have to keep your wits about you and know your seven times table to keep up with this fast-paced game.

WHAT YOU MUST DO:

The players sit in a circle or around a table. The first player starts off saying 'one', the next says 'two', the next 'three' and so on round the table until you reach seven. Instead of seven, you must say 'buzz'.

You must also say 'buzz' on multiples of seven – 14, 21, 28, 35 and upwards – as well as any number that has seven in it – 17, 27, 37 and upwards. When you get to 77, you have to say 'buzz-buzz'.

If you say a number when you should say 'buzz,' or think about it too long, you are out of the game. The last player left is the winner.

TIP
If it starts to get too easy only using seven as buzz, then why not also try buzzing on numbers that are multiples of nine or have nine in them.

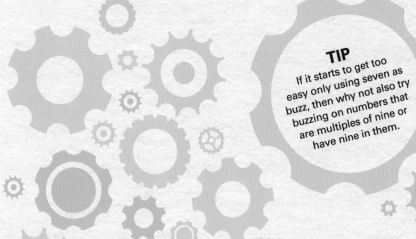

78. OLD PALS

A man named George was walking through his local town centre when he bumped into an old university friend he hadn't seen for years.

They stopped and chatted for a while, catching up on old times.

'I married someone you don't know,' said his friend, 'and this is our daughter.'

The little girl said hello to George, who asked her what her name was.

'It's the same as my mummy's,' she replied.

'Then you are called Sarah!' said George.

HOW DID HE KNOW?

Solution on page 215

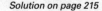

79. RICH AND POOR

Poor people have me, rich people
need me and if you eat me you will starve.

WHAT AM I?

Solution on page 215

80. MISSING NUMBER

1, 11, 21, 1211, 111221, - - - - - -

Complete the sequence.

Solution on page 215

81. OVERTAKING

Solution on page 215

If you overtake the person in second place in a race,

WHAT POSITION ARE YOU NOW IN?

82. SHORT IS BIG

The shorter I am, the bigger
and more frightening I am.

WHAT AM I?

Solution on page 215

83. GET KNOTTED

2+ players
Don't get yourself all tied in knots when you try out this party trick – it's a lot simpler than it seems.

WHAT YOU WILL NEED:

- A standard, square cloth table napkin

WHAT YOU MUST DO:

Tell your friends that you can pick a napkin up off the table, taking an end in each hand, and tie a knot in the middle without letting go of either end. They will not believe you, but here's how it's done.

Place the napkin on the table in front of you, neatly folded in a triangle. Now stand in front of the napkin and fold your arms. Without unfolding your arms, bend down to the left and grab the left corner of the triangle in your right hand. Bend the other way and grab the right corner in your left hand.

Stand up straight and draw your arms apart, pulling your right hand to the right and your left hand to the left, without letting go of the napkin ends.

When your arms are completely unfolded, the napkin will have a knot in the middle.

TIP
Trying to pick up the napkin feels really awkward at first, but once you have done it a couple of times it gets much easier.

84. LONG WEEKEND

A traveller on a long journey rides into a small village in the heart of the countryside.

He rides in on Friday and checks in to the only hotel in town. He stays for three nights, then rides out again on Friday.

HOW CAN THIS BE?

Solution on page 215

85. IT'S BEHIND YOU!

What is always behind you but never more than a day away?

HINT
Sometimes the answer to a question like this is far more obvious than you might think.

Solution on page 215

86. NUMBER SQUARE

The digits 1, 2, 3, 4, 5, 6, 7, 8 and 9 must be put in this square in such a way that the sums of the numbers in each row, column and diagonal are equal.

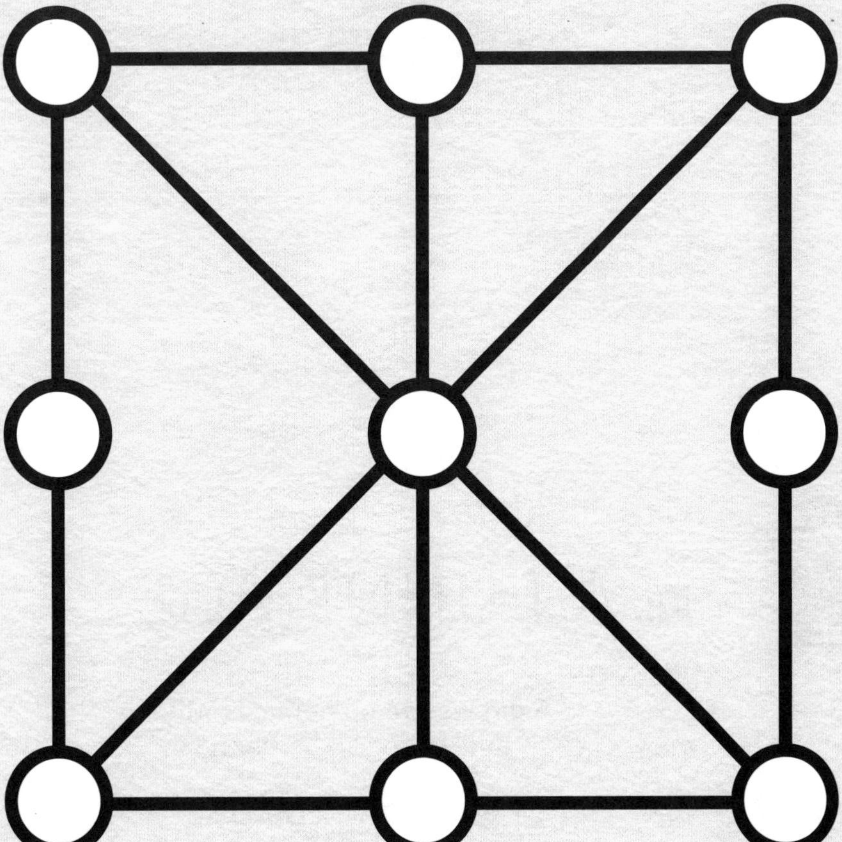

Solution on page 215

87. STAIR RACE

I run upstairs ahead of you and
always reach the bottom of
the stairs before you.

WHAT AM I?

Solution on page 215

88. A FUNNY AGE

A girl was 14 on her last birthday
and will be 16 on her next.

HOW IS THIS POSSIBLE?

Solution on page 215

89. PICTURE THIS

4+ players
There is no quiet way of playing this game, so be prepared for a lively, noisy time and lots of laughs!

WHAT YOU WILL NEED:

- Pencil and paper
- A stopwatch

WHAT YOU MUST DO:

This game is like Charades (see p14). The player trying to convey the title of a book, play, movie, song or TV show can't make a sound and is not allowed to make any gestures or do any acting. Instead, they have to draw clues on a piece of paper.

Players are divided into two teams and one team must write down a title. This is then given to one of the players from the other team who must not show the title to the rest of his or her team.

Using a different sheet of paper, the player has to draw a book, a stage with curtains, a movie camera, a singing face or a TV to give the team their first clue.

The player then marks a series of dashes on the paper, one for each letter of the title, with a / to show a break between words.

The player points to a word, or even a letter, and draws something to represent that word. If the title was *Charlie and the Chocolate Factory*, the player could show that it was a book, a movie and a play, point to the last word and try to draw a factory.

Players have to be quick on the draw, because they have just five minutes to get their team to come up with the answer. After that, the other team gets to have a go. The team with the most correct answers at the end of the evening is the winner.

90. STRING RELAY

6+ players
In most races, you need strong legs and stamina to come first, but this race relies more on nimble fingers.

WHAT YOU WILL NEED:

- Two pieces of string (the more players you have, the longer the strings need to be)

WHAT YOU MUST DO:

Nominate a Starter who will say 'Go!' to start the relay race. The players are divided into two relay teams and must sit on the floor or at a table in a line.

The first player in each team holds their piece of string and when the starter calls 'Go!' player 1 ties a knot in the string and passes it to player 2, who does the same.

The last player ties a knot and the string is passed all the way back to the first player, who unties one knot. Each player in turn unties a knot and the last player passes the untied string back to player 1.

The first team to have a knot-free piece of string back in the hands of their first player is the winner.

TIP
Don't get overexcited and tie your knots too tight or it will take ages to untie them again.

91. A PIECE OF CAKE

How do you divide a circular birthday cake into eight equal pieces using only three straight cuts and without moving any pieces?

Solution on page 215

92. BIG BREAK

What has to be broken before you can use it?

HINT
I can promise you, without breaking my promise, that some people break these every day!

Solution on page 215

93. BATTLESHIPS

2+ players
Destroy your enemy's fleet without leaving the comfort of your own living room.

WHAT YOU WILL NEED:

- Pencil and paper for each player

WHAT YOU MUST DO:

Each player marks out two 10 x 10 grids. Down the left the rows are numbered 1 to 10. Across the top the columns are lettered A to J. One grid is labelled 'Home Fleet', the other 'Enemy Fleet.'

On the 'Home Fleet' grid, you must now deploy your ships without letting your enemy see. Each player has one battleship which covers four squares, two cruisers (three squares each), three destroyers (two squares each) and four submarines (one square each). Your ships must be marked horizontally or vertically, not diagonally, and must not be touching.

Decide who goes first and then take turns to fire at your enemy's ships by calling out a square using a grid reference. F6, for example, is column F, row 6. If part of an enemy ship occupies that square, the other player must call out 'Hit!' If it is an empty square the call is 'Miss!' If you score a hit, your opponent must tell you what you have hit and you get to have another go. If it's a miss, it's his turn to fire at you.

If you score a 'miss', remember to mark it on your Enemy Fleet grid. Shade the square or write 'M' for miss, so that you know there is no ship in that square and you won't fire at it again.

You need four hits to sink a battleship, three to sink a cruiser, two for a destroyer and one for a sub. The first one to sink all their enemy's ships is the winner.

	A	B	C	D	E	F	G	H	I	J
1								S		
2		B	B	B	B					
3									S	
4		D	D				D			
5							D			
6	S									
7				D	D				C	
8									C	
9		C	C	C					C	
10						S				

HOME FLEET

	A	B	C	D	E	F	G	H	I	J
1		S						D		S
2								D		
3			C	C	C					
4								C	C	C
5										
6		D	D						B	
7					D				B	
8					D				B	
9			S						B	
10	S									

ENEMY FLEET

S 4x Submarines (one square)

D D 3x Destroyers (two squares)

C C C 2x Cruisers (three squares)

B B B B 1x Battleship (four squares)

S X - Hit/Sunk Submarines

D D X - Hit/Sunk Destroyers

C C C X - Hit/Sunk Cruisers

B B B B X - Hit/Sunk Battleship

94. BORDER DILEMMA

Why can't a man living in England be legally buried in Scotland?

Solution on page 216

95. NEVER SHARE

If you have one you can keep it
forever, but if you share one
it will no longer exist.

WHAT IS IT?

Solution on page 216

96. THE COWBOYS' HATS

Three cowboys rode into a town in the wild west.
One had a black horse and wore brown boots.
One had a white horse and wore black boots.
One had a brown horse and wore white boots.

WHICH ONE WORE THE BIGGEST HAT?

Solution on page 216

97. ONE-WAY

A policeman sees a bus driver is going against the traffic down a one-way street but does not stop him.

WHY NOT?

Solution on page 216

98. VANISHING COTTON BUD

2+ players
Make an ordinary cotton bud disappear from your hand right in front of your audience!

WHAT YOU WILL NEED:

- A cotton bud
- Scissors
- A small piece of double-sided sticky tape

WHAT YOU MUST DO:

This magic trick can be performed with your audience quite close, but you must keep your hands moving and keep talking to distract their attention.

The one piece of preparation that you have to do is to attach the double-sided sticky tape to the thumbnail on your right hand. Trim the tape so that it neatly covers your thumbnail.

Show the cotton bud to your audience, holding it in your left hand and keeping your hands on the move. You don't want anyone to spot that tape. You can even give the cotton bud to someone in the audience to inspect so that they know it is a real cotton bud.

Then, holding the cotton bud in your left hand, place it in your right hand as though you are gripping it in your fist. The audience will still see the top of the cotton bud sticking up, but they will not see your right thumb folded down behind your fingers, with your fingers pressing the bud against the sticky tape.

Don't hold the bud like that for more than a moment or two, otherwise someone may notice that your thumb is in a strange place. Distract the audience by talking and waving your left hand about, then slap your left hand into your right fist and quickly open both hands, showing them palms out to your audience. The cotton bud will appear to have gone, but it is actually hidden behind your right thumb.

Wave your hands around, keeping your palms towards the audience, and snatch your right hand down in front of you, forming a fist as before to make it look like you have just plucked the bud out of the air.

You can use your left hand quickly to pull the bud off the tape and hand it back to one of your amazed audience.

1.

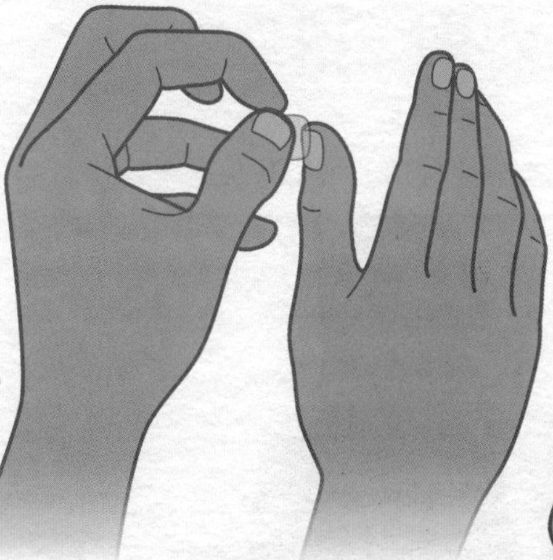

1. Put double-sided sticky tape on your thumbnail. The neater you make it, the less obvious it will be.

2.

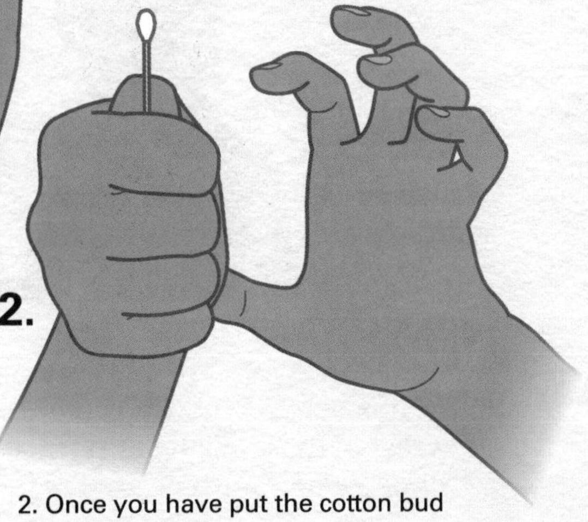

2. Once you have put the cotton bud in your right hand, keep your left hand moving to distract the audience.

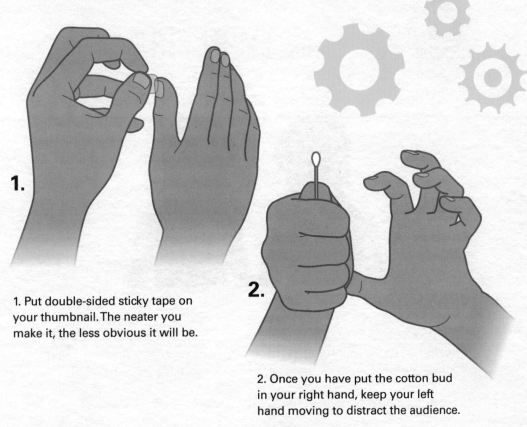

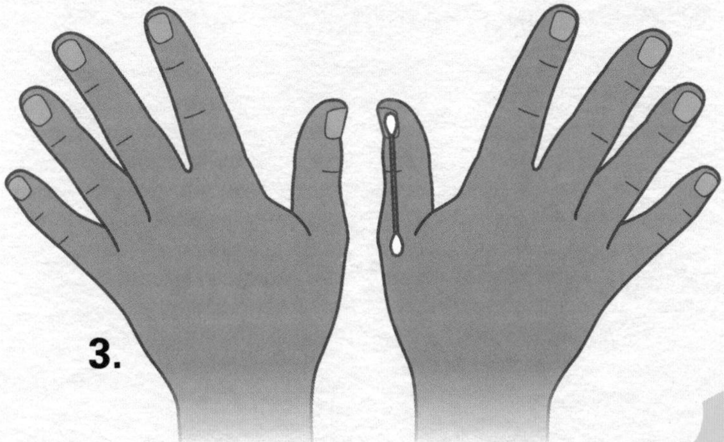

3.

3. This is how it will look from your point of view. Your audience will see only your empty hands.

TIP

Keep your hands on the move to distract your audience's attention, but be careful not to let them see behind your thumb where the cotton bud is hiding.

99. TWIN FIBS

Twins Billy and Tom are in the same class at school. Both are known to tell fibs but Billy only lies on Monday, Tuesday and Wednesday – the rest of the week he tells the truth. Tom only lies on Thursday, Friday and Saturday – the rest of the week he tells the truth.

Billy says: 'Yesterday I was lying.' Tom says: 'So was I.'

WHO IS TELLING THE TRUTH?

Solution on page 216

100. WET OR DRY

What gets bigger the more it dries?

Solution on page 216

101. UPS AND DOWNS

What can go up a chimney down but not down a chimney up?

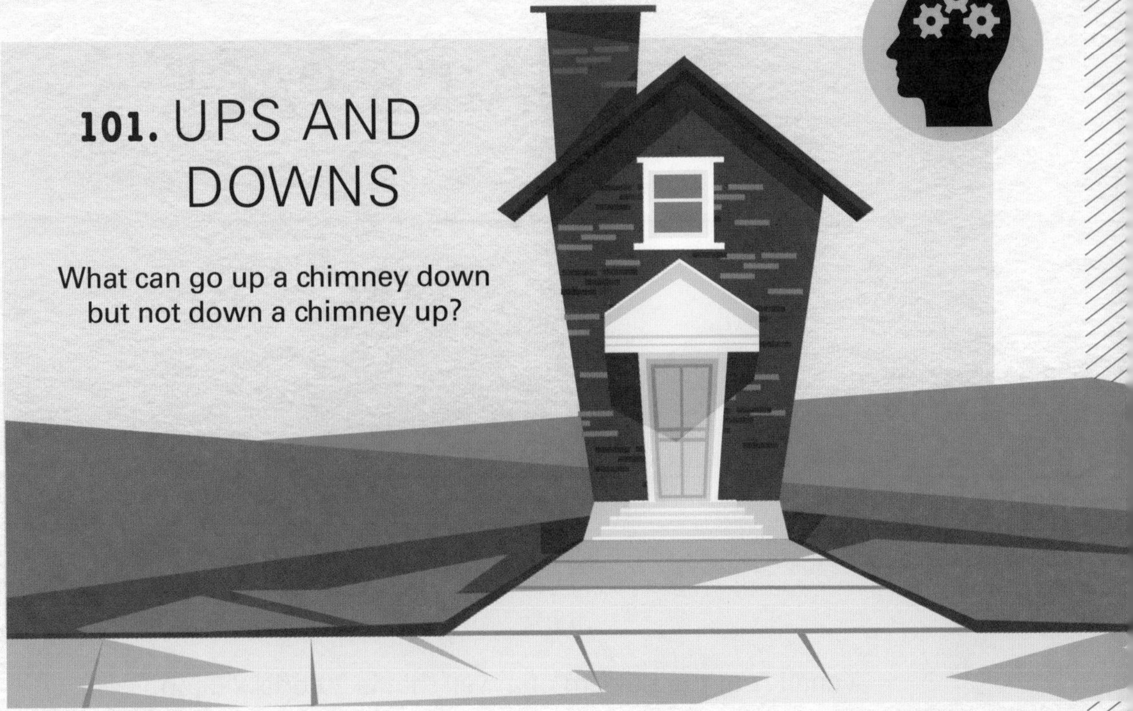

Solution on page 216

102. STRANGE PLACES

Where can you find rivers with no fish, roads with no cars, seas with no ships and towns with no people?

Solution on page 216

HINT

This sounds like a real disaster but it's more likely to help get you out of trouble than to land you in it.

103. SNAIL'S PACE

A snail is at the bottom of a well that is 20 bricks deep. Every day the snail climbs 5 bricks up the side of the well, but every night it slides back 4 bricks again.

WHAT DAY DOES IT REACH THE TOP?

Solution on page 216

104. NO QUESTIONS ASKED

What asks no questions but must always be answered?

HINT
Thinking of home might ring a bell.

Solution on page 216

105. WORD RACE

2+ players
You have to be able to spell simple words to take part in this game, and be able to spot places to create them.

WHAT YOU WILL NEED:

- Paper and pencils for each player
- A dictionary (optional)

WHAT YOU MUST DO:

Each player writes down all of the letters of the alphabet on his or her sheet of paper. A ten-square by ten-square grid is then drawn on a separate sheet.

The first player then writes a word horizontally as close to the middle of the grid as possible. You can only use letters from your alphabet (so no double letters) and you score off the letters as you use them so you can't use them again.

The next player then writes a word vertically that intersects with the first word. Words must always intersect and players continue to take turns. If you can't think of a word to use, you miss a turn.

Play continues until someone wins by using up all of his or her letters, but it is more likely that you will reach the stage where no one can think of a word using the letters they have left. Once you agree to call a halt, the player with the fewest letters left wins.

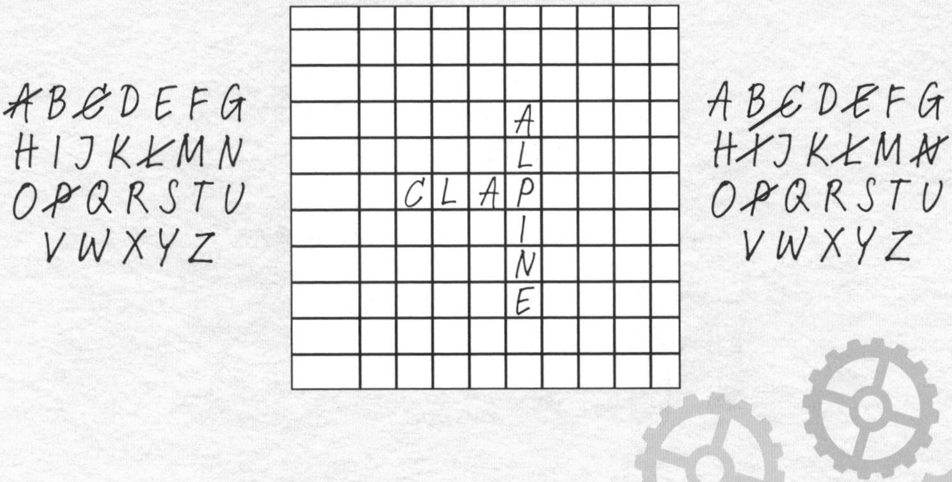

106. CAR CODES

2+ players
When you are stuck in traffic on a long and tedious car journey, this game is silly enough to raise a few smiles.

WHAT YOU WILL NEED:

- A traffic jam
- A stopwatch

WHAT YOU MUST DO:

One person in the car is nominated as the Chief Code Breaker and the Chief Code Breaker points out number plates of nearby cars to each player, or Spy, in turn.

The Spy must study the letters in the number plate (ignore the numbers) and work out a coded message they might represent – the sillier the better.

For example, a number plate that has letters in the order KPFD could be 'Kevin's Partly Full Doughnuts' or 'King's Pants Falling Down'.

If a Spy fails to come up with a coded message within 20 seconds, as timed by the Chief Code Breaker, he or she is out and the winner is the last Spy left. The last Spy then becomes the new Chief Code Breaker and you start all over again.

107. MISSING LETTERS

Solution on page 216

What are the next three letters
in the following sequence?

JFM AMJ JAS ---

108. THE READER

A man sits by a window reading. No light is switched on in the room, there is no moon outside and he has no torch, lamp or candle, yet he can still see to read.

HOW IS THIS POSSIBLE?

Solution on page 216

109. UPTURNED GLASSES

These seven glasses are all in a row and all upside down. Your challenge is to turn them all the right way up in the least possible moves. You must always turn over three glasses in one move.

HOW MANY MOVES ARE REQUIRED?

Solution on page 216

HINT
Once you have turned a glass over, it needn't stay that way.

110. LORD OF THE RING

2+ players
If you have a good aim and a steady hand, you can become the Lord (or Lady!) of the Ring in this classic marbles game.

WHAT YOU WILL NEED:

- Marbles – three for each player
- A length of cotton thread or a sheet of newspaper

WHAT YOU MUST DO:

Each player is given three marbles. If they can all be the same colour or pattern, that is good but not vital.

A circle needs to be marked on the ground. If you are outside, you can scratch a rough circle with a stick in the dirt to make a target ring. If you are playing inside, you can arrange the length of cotton on the floor to make a target ring. If no cotton is available, a sheet of newspaper can be laid down to make your target area.

Each player then puts one marble inside the ring, positioning it wherever they like. The players then take it in turns to 'shoot' one of their remaining marbles at the marbles in the ring. You can shoot by flicking the marble out of your hand with your thumb, or by rolling it along the ground. You must all shoot from the same point an agreed distance from the ring.

The object is to knock one or more of the marbles out of the ring. Players keep any marbles that they knock out of the ring. If you shoot and miss, you can collect your shooting marble from wherever it lands, unless it stops inside the ring, in which case you must leave it there. When you next shoot, you will then have to use one of your other marbles until you are down to your last one. Lose that and you are out of the game.

The winner is the player who ends up with the most marbles when there are none left in the ring.

111. TWENTY QUESTIONS

3+ players
Telling the truth but still keeping your secret is a real challenge when you are faced with questioners determined to find out what you are thinking.

WHAT YOU MUST DO:

The aim of the game is to find out a secret word that one of the players is thinking. The other players are allowed to ask questions, to work out the secret word, but if they can't guess it after 20 questions have been asked, the player with the secret wins the game.

One player has to be selected to start and must think of a word. It can be something in the room, something from the outside world, an animal, a car, a movie star – anything at all.

The others then take it in turns to ask questions. At first, the questions need to be quite general in order to get them thinking along the right lines. 'Is it a living thing?' might be one, or 'Is it a machine?'

The player with the secret is only allowed to answer 'Yes' or 'No.' No other clues can be given. If the answer to 'Is it a living thing?' was yes, then the next question might be 'Is it an animal?' followed by 'Does it live on a farm?'

When one of the players thinks he or she knows what the secret word is, that player's next question should be a guess, such as, 'Is it a donkey?' If the guess is wrong, that player is out of the game for the remainder of the round. If the guess is right, that player is the winner and is the next one to think of a secret word.

112. NUMBER CIRCLES

The numbers 1 to 16 must be placed in the circles of the square below in such a way that the sum of the numbers in each row, column, and diagonal amounts to 34.

HOW SHOULD THE NUMBERS BE ARRANGED IN THE SQUARE?

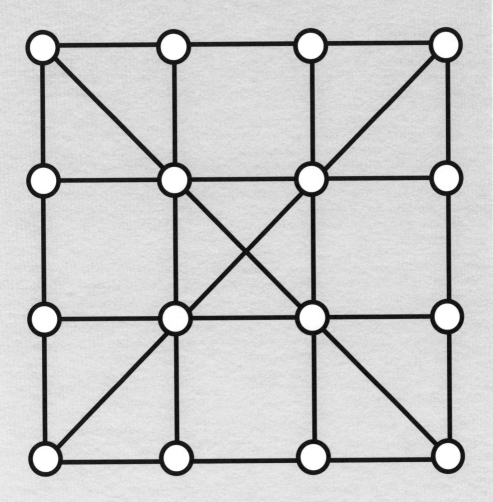

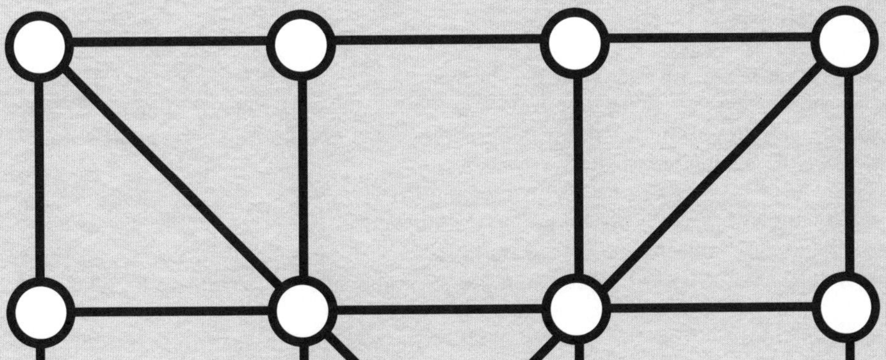

Solution on page 216

113. DISSOLVING COIN

2+ players
Can a coin magically dissolve beneath an empty wine glass? If you can perfect this trick, then of course it can!

WHAT YOU WILL NEED:

- A wine glass • A coin • A pencil
- Three identical sheets of coloured paper
- Scissors • A cloth • Double-sided sticky tape

WHAT YOU MUST DO:

This trick requires careful secret preparation and a little practice if you are to make it work flawlessly. The first thing that you have to do is to prepare your wine glass. Place the glass upside down on one of your identical sheets of coloured paper and draw round it very carefully with a sharp pencil.

You will be left with a circle on the paper. Cut out this circle, making sure that you follow the line precisely. Now cut four thin pieces of double-sided sticky tape. You should aim to make them no wider than the thickness of the rim of the wine glass.

Stick the tape to the rim of the glass. If there is any excess, either trim it off or make sure that it folds up inside the glass. It shouldn't show if there is only a tiny amount. You should position the sticky tape at four points around the rim – where 12, 3, 6 and 9 would be on a clock face.

Now press the rim down onto the disc of coloured paper that you cut out. The rim should fit exactly over the disc. When you stand the wine glass on its base, it should look like illustration 2.

You are now ready to set up your trick. Your audience must not see that the mouth of the wine glass is covered with coloured paper, so you have to set up the trick in advance, perhaps on a tray that you can carry into the room.

You should have two sheets of coloured paper lying side by side. The wine glass stands upside down on one sheet, and on the other sheet you place an ordinary coin.

Cover the wine glass with a cloth and say your favourite magic words before you pick it up, still covered with the cloth so that the audience can't see the coloured paper stuck to it, and place it on the other sheet of paper.

With a few more magic words and hand waving, you can remove the cloth and the wine glass will be standing in place, but the coin will appear to have vanished, although actually it is just hidden beneath the paper that you stuck to the wine glass.

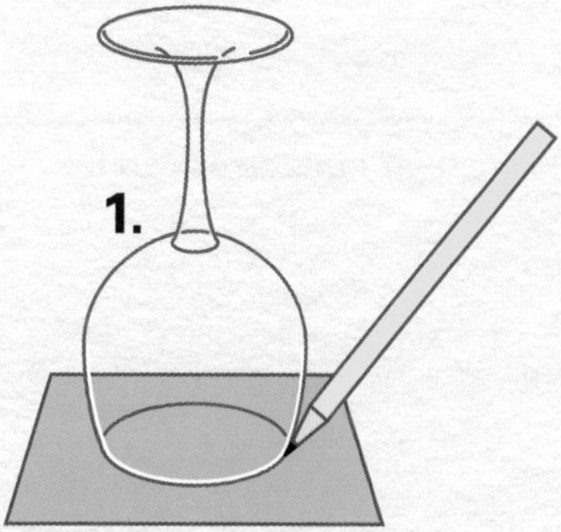

1.

1. Carefully draw around the upturned glass as accurately as you can.

2.

2. Cut out the disc of coloured paper so that it can be stuck neatly over the top of the glass.

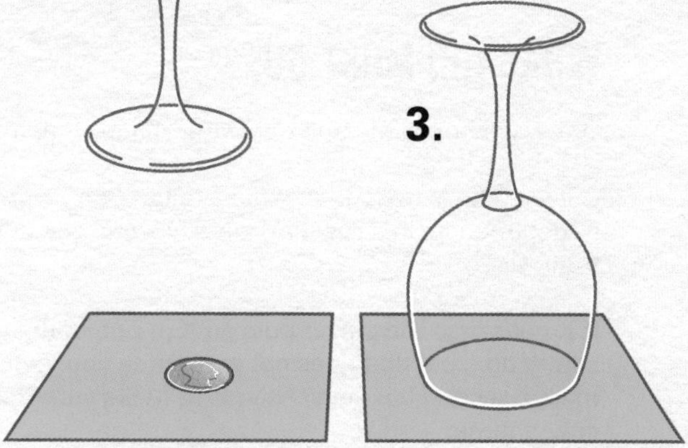

3.

3. When the upturned glass sits on a fresh sheet of coloured paper, the disc will not be noticed.

4. Cover the glass with a napkin before you move it, and when you remove the napkin, the disc will be hiding the coin as though it has vanished.

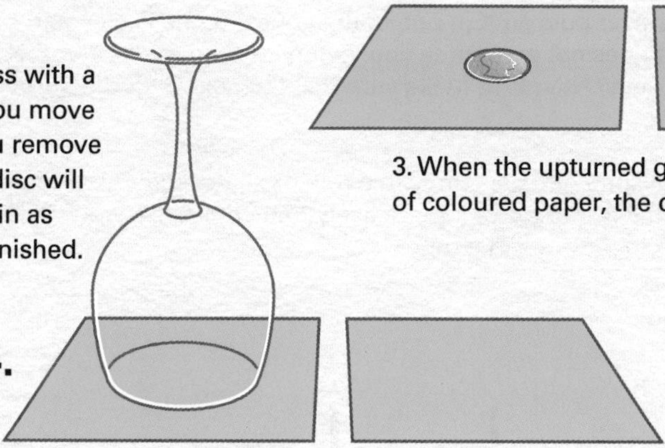

4.

TIP

The essential thing is to cut and attach the disc neatly. Any rough edges will be noticed when the glass is standing on one of the other sheets of coloured paper.

114. NOUGHTS & CROSSES

2+ players
If you play this game fast, you have to think fast and mistakes can be made that will cost you a win.

WHAT YOU WILL NEED:

- Paper
- Two pencils

WHAT YOU MUST DO:

Draw two horizontal and two vertical lines that intersect to form a grid of nine squares.

Decide who is to go first, who is to be X and who is to be O. If you are X, your aim is to get three Xs in a row horizontally, vertically or diagonally. If you are O, you want three Os.

If X goes first, the player puts an X in one of the boxes. Some like to start by taking the centre box, but that does not guarantee you victory. O then marks a box. X must now mark a second box and O needs to make sure that the next O blocks X from making a line of three.

So it continues until someone gets three in a row or all the squares are full. Take turns at going first and play fast to make it more likely that your opponent will make a mistake and let you in for three in a row.

115. BLIND MAN'S BUFF

2+ players
A bit of clear floor space is required for this game to make sure that your 'blind man' (or woman) doesn't go crashing into the furniture.

WHAT YOU WILL NEED:

- A blindfold

WHAT YOU MUST DO:

One player is chosen to be the first to wear the blindfold. Once blindfolded, the player is spun round three times and everyone else scatters out of reach.

The blindfolded player now staggers around the room trying to catch hold of any one of the other players. The other players move about, make as much noise as they like, give the blindfolded player false directions and can even dart in to give a tickle or gently tug a sleeve if they are brave enough to risk being caught.

When the blindfolded player catches someone, the captured player must not speak as the one wearing the blindfold has to identify his prisoner by touch alone.

If the blindfolded player guesses correctly, the captured player takes the blindfold and the game starts again. If he or she guesses wrongly, the prisoner is released and the 'blind man' has to catch someone else.

116. WINK MURDER

5+ players
An easily portable game, you can play Wink Murder in your living room, on a picnic or anywhere that you can gather enough people together around a table or sitting in a circle.

WHAT YOU WILL NEED:

- A pack of cards

WHAT YOU MUST DO:

You have to count out as many cards as there are players. These can be any cards but must include the ace of spades and the ace of hearts. The players look at their cards but must not show anyone else.

The player who gets the ace of hearts is the detective and must tell everyone. The player who gets the ace of spades is the murderer and, like all of the other players, stays silent. The players now talk to each other while the detective tries to discover who the murderer is by seeing him or her winking.

The murderer has to blend in with the other players but, when he or she catches a player's eye and winks, that player has been murdered and can make a great show of dying with shrieks, groans and a lot of flopping around. Basically, if you are killed, die as dramatically as possible.

The detective has to spot the murderer before all the other players fall victim and, obviously, nobody else is allowed to wink. Once the murderer is caught, or only the detective and the murderer are left, you can start all over again.

117. DROWNING IN SOCKS

You have a really muddled sock drawer that is stuffed full of different-coloured socks. You have 2 red, 4 yellow, 6 purple, 8 brown, 10 white, 12 green, 14 black, 16 blue, 18 grey and 20 orange socks. Without looking, how many socks do you need to take out of the drawer to be sure that you have at least three pairs of socks of the same colour?

Solution on page 217

118. HOW MANY AUNTS?

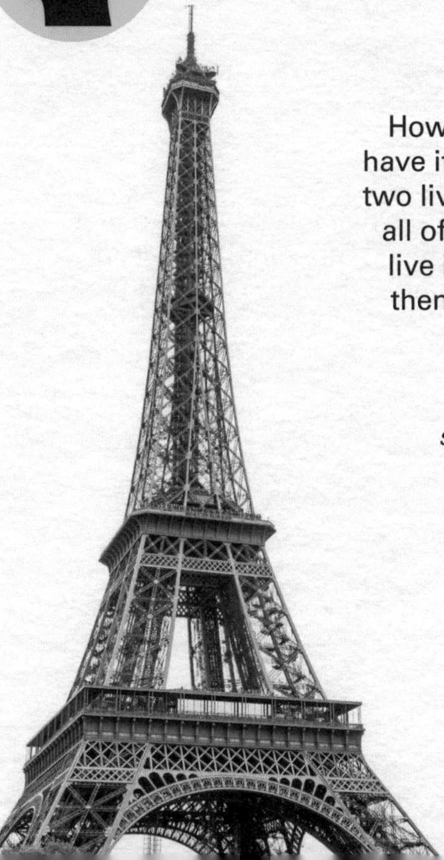

How many aunts do I have if all of them except two live in New York, and all of them except two live in Paris and all of them except two live in London?

Solution on page 217

119. HALF A GLASS

You have a glass of water that you think is half full. Assuming that the glass is a perfect cylinder, and using no other implements or instruments, how can you tell accurately if the glass is half full?

Solution on page 217

120. BINGO

2+ players
Be the first to check off all your numbers and call 'BINGO!'

WHAT YOU WILL NEED:

- Paper for each player • Paper for making numbers
- Pencils for each player • Scissors • A bag or hat

WHAT YOU MUST DO:

Each player draws a grid nine boxes wide by three boxes deep, making 27 boxes in total. Players then mark five numbers in each of the three rows, leaving four random spaces each time, but the numbers must be marked in a specific way.

In the first column, you can have only numbers from 1 to 10. In the second column, you can have only numbers from 11 to 20. In the third column you have numbers from 21 to 30, and so on across the nine columns, with numbers from 81 to 90 at the end. You must not use a number more than once. This traditional style of numbering, along wih the blank spaces, spreads the random numbers as evenly as possible, giving everyone an equal chance of winning.

A 'caller' must be chosen and this player draws another grid ten squares by nine squares, writing a number from 1 to 90 in each box. This grid must then be cut up to make lots of little numbered squares.

The caller puts all of these numbers into the bag or hat and then the game begins. The caller takes one number from the hat and calls it out. If you have that number on your grid, you cross it out. The caller then takes another number from the hat and play continues in this way until one player has crossed out all of their numbers and calls out 'BINGO!'

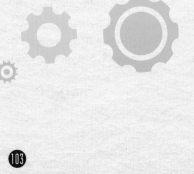

121. WHAT'S MISSING?

What is the missing part of this sequence?

16 06 68 88 ?? 98

Solution on page 217

122. DAYS GONE BY

When the day after tomorrow is yesterday, today will be as far from Wednesday as today was from Wednesday when the day before yesterday was tomorrow.

WHAT IS TOMORROW?

Solution on page 217

123. WHO'S AT THE PARTY?

2+ players
It's a strange sort of party where everyone knows everyone else but none of the guests know who they are!

WHAT YOU WILL NEED:

- Pencil
- Sticky notes (or paper and sticky tape)

WHAT YOU MUST DO:

Each player must write the name of a famous person – or a character from a book, play, song, movie or TV show – on a sticky note without anyone seeing what they have written. They each then stick the name to the forehead of the player next to them, without letting that player see what the name is.

When everyone has a name on their forehead, everyone can see everyone else's name, but not their own. Players must take it in turns to ask a question about 'themselves', such as 'Am I a man?' or 'Do I appear on TV?' or 'Do I have red hair?' The other players shout out 'Yes!' or 'No!' If the answer is yes, the player immediately gets to ask another question, if not, it is the next player's turn to ask about himself or herself.

Once a player has asked enough questions to know that she is a female singer who has also appeared in movies and is still in the news, the player might want to use their next question to guess 'Am I Madonna?' If that's the name on the sticky then that player has won, but the game goes on until everyone has guessed who they are.

124. MILLENNIUM

2+ players
Like the Century game on page 18, Millennium involves keeping count of the score, but this time the numbers are bigger.

WHAT YOU WILL NEED:

- Six dice
- Pencil and paper

WHAT YOU MUST DO:

Players take turns to throw the dice. A player throws all six dice at once and scores only if the dice show a sequence or multiple numbers. Players earn points for rolling sequences or multiples as follows:

Sequence of three (1,2,3 or 2,3,4 or 3,4,5 or 4,5,6)	250 points
Sequence of four (1,2,3,4 or 2,3,4,5 or 3,4,5,6)	500 points
Sequence of five (1,2,3,4,5 or 2,3,4,5,6)	750 points
Sequence of six	1,000 points
Three of a kind	250 points
Four of a kind	500 points
Five of a kind	750 points
Six of a kind	1,000 points

It is possible on one roll to be able to count more than one score – a sequence of three and three of a kind, for example. If this happens you count both scores. A sequence of three and three of a kind would score 500 points. A sequence of four and three of a kind would score 750.

First player to reach 1,000 points or more is the winner.

TIP
Keep up with the scoring to ensure that everyone is writing down their score correctly. It's easy to make mistakes with big numbers when things are moving quickly.

125. NEVER YES

To what question can the answer never be
YES?

Solution on page 217

126. MYSTERY OBJECT

I cannot talk. I cannot walk or crawl. I come into a room but I never sit on the furniture, yet I never leave.

WHAT AM I?

Solution on page 217

127. FAMILY FUN

At a family party, a grandfather, a grandmother, two fathers, two mothers, four children, three grandchildren, one brother, two sisters, two sons, two daughters, one father-in-law, one mother-in-law and one daughter-in-law sit at a table.

HOW MANY PEOPLE ARE AT THE TABLE?

Solution on page 217

128. WALK ON BY

It walks on four legs in the morning, two legs at midday and three legs in the evening.

WHAT IS IT?

HINT

This is one of the world's most ancient riddles and the answer may seem strange to us in the modern world. It is an interesting riddle, nonetheless.

Solution on page 217

129. THREE-IN-A-ROW

2+ players
There's an element of skill involved in this game but your skill develops quickly after just a few sessions.

WHAT YOU WILL NEED:

- Paper and pencil
- Six counters – two different coloured sets of three

WHAT YOU MUST DO:

Draw your Three-in-a-Row pitch on a piece of paper by copying the diagram shown below.

When you have decided who is to go first, that player places a counter at a point on the board where lines intersect. The other player then places a counter at a different intersection. The aim is to get three counters in a row and to stop your opponent getting three in a row. In that respect, this is a little like noughts and crosses.

If no one has won once both players have placed all three of their counters, they then take it in turns to move one counter along a line to the next intersection, in any direction, provided that intersection is not already occupied. They still need three in a row to win. If you reach the stage where no one can make a move, the game is a draw.

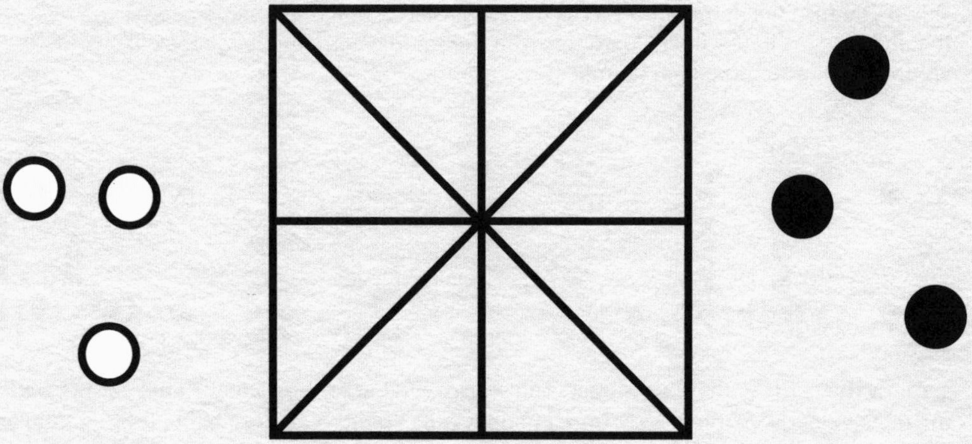

130. CATCH THE QUEEN

2+ players
You can fool a friend with this simple party trick once, but the queen probably won't escape a second time.

WHAT YOU WILL NEED:

- Five ordinary playing cards, including one queen
- A paperclip
- Some glue or sticky tape (optional)

WHAT YOU MUST DO:

Arrange the cards as shown in the first illustration, with the queen in the middle. To make it easier for you when you are showing people this trick, you might want to put a few spots of glue on the cards or use some sticky tape to hold them together in this formation. This isn't part of the trick and you can show everyone that the cards are stuck together, or even tell everyone that sticking the cards together means that there's no way you can secretly switch them around.

Show your audience the cards face out so that they can see that the queen is in the middle, then turn the cards the other way round, so that they can see only the backs.

Now ask for a volunteer, hand your volunteer the paperclip and ask him or her to 'catch the queen' by putting a paperclip over the queen. Most people will, at first, choose the middle card, as seen from the back, and place the clip as shown in the second illustration.

When you turn the cards round to face your audience again, the paperclip will be over the end card, as in the final illustration, not the middle card and it will look like your volunteer missed the queen by miles!

1. 

1. Show the cards with the queen clearly visible in the middle.

2. 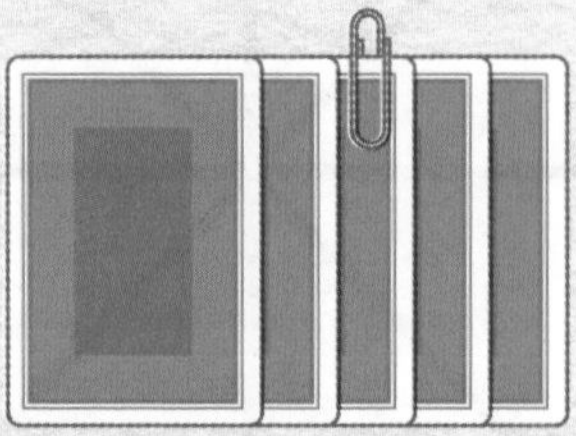

2. When shown the backs, most people will clip the middle card.

3. 

3. Turn the cards back to show they've totally missed the queen.

131. EXACT DELIVERY

A milkman has an order for delivery of exactly one gallon of milk. He must not deliver more than a gallon and he must not deliver less than a gallon.

He has a large tank of fresh milk but only two empty jugs – a 3-gallon jug and a 5-gallon jug.

HOW CAN HE MEASURE EXACTLY ONE GALLON WITHOUT WASTING ANY MILK?

Solution on page 218

132. WORD LADDERS

2+ players
This is a traditional game that requires a little thought and is very rewarding when you make it work.

WHAT YOU WILL NEED:

- Paper and pencil for each player
- A stopwatch

WHAT YOU MUST DO:

This is a race with each player competing to be first to finish the word ladder, not in the least time but in the least number of steps. If the challenge is, for example, to change COW to PIG, one letter at a time, creating a new word at each stage, one solution is COW-COG-DOG-DIG-PIG.

The words must all have the same number of letters and the minimum number of steps on your word ladder is the same as the number of letters in the word. You may often, however, need to take far more than the minimum number of steps.

It is more fun to choose first and last words that have some sort of link, like SEED and TREE (SEED-SLED-FLED-FLEE-FREE-TREE) or BOY to MAN (BOY-BAY-MAY-MAN).

Although the first person to find a solution may not have found the most direct route – BOY to MAN could be BOY-TOY-TON-TAN-MAN, one step more than above – you can't wait around forever trying to work out the shortest route, so it's best to set a time limit of five minutes.

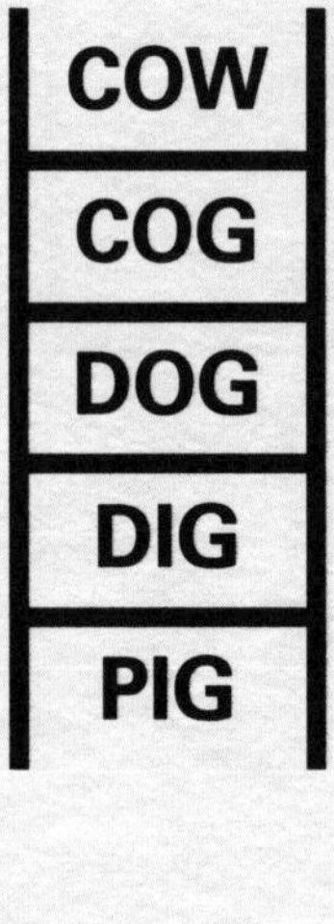

If no one can find a solution after five minutes, set another word ladder challenge.

133. THE MAGIC STRAW

2+ players
Make a straw spin on a bottle top without touching it.

WHAT YOU WILL NEED:

- A plastic drinking straw
- A plastic bottle with the cap in place
- Wool sweater or fleece

WHAT YOU MUST DO:

Rub the drinking straw on your sweater, swiping it several times. Only touch the straw with one hand and hold it at one end.

Now balance the straw on top of the bottle and immediately move your hand away.

Move a finger close to the straw and it will start to move towards your finger. Move your finger around the bottle and the straw will spin on top. Be gentle, or the straw may fall off the bottle, but do not let the straw touch your finger.

Rubbing the straw creates static electricity and gives the straw a negative electrical charge. When you hold your finger close to the end of the straw, the straw is attracted to the positive charge on your skin in the same way that opposite ends of a magnet are attracted.

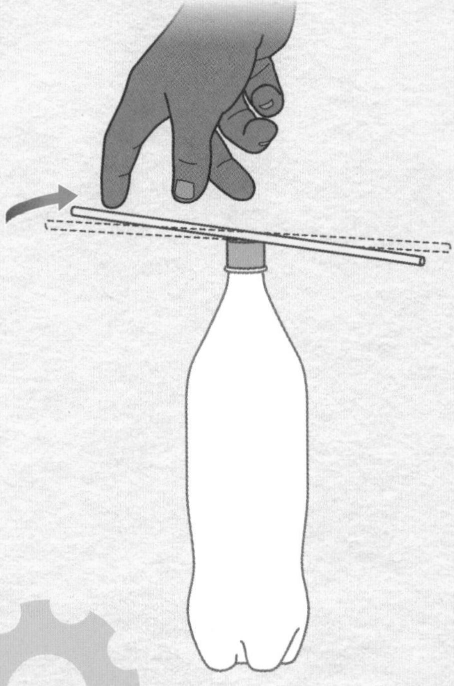

134. TOOTHPICK MATHS

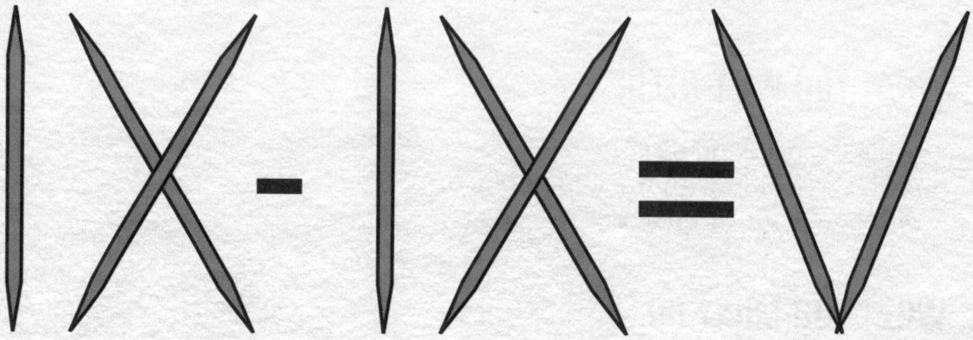

Move one toothpick to correct the sum

Solution on page 218

HINT

You'll need to know your Roman numerals to solve this problem. Think where you can move your toothpick to create a new numeral – or change an existing one.

135. AGE IN NUMBERS

When asked how old he is, a child replies:
In four years, I will be twice as old as I was three years ago.
And a year after that I will be three times as old as I was five years ago.

HOW OLD IS HE?

Solution on page 218

136. BIRTHDAY BRAIN BUSTER

Twin sisters each give birth to a son at exactly the same moment, yet the boys have different birthdays.

HOW CAN THIS BE?

Solution on page 218

137. THE TRAVELLER

As I was going to St Ives
I met a man with seven wives
Each wife had seven sacks
Each sack had seven cats
Each cat had seven kits
Kits, cats, sacks, wives

HOW MANY WERE GOING TO ST IVES?

Solution on page 218

HINT
To solve this riddle, think about what it's actually telling you – not what you think it's telling you!

138. ALPHABET MARKET

2+ players
You will have some strange items on your shopping list by the end of this game.

WHAT YOU WILL NEED:

- A good memory

WHAT YOU MUST DO:

The first player begins by saying, 'I went to the market and bought a ...' and must list something beginning with the letter A. The next player must list something beginning with B, but also has to say what the item beginning with A was, and so on, working your way through the alphabet.

Player 1: I went to the market and bought an ... apricot.
Player 2: I went to the market and bought an apricot and a bag.
Player 3: I went to the market and bought an apricot, a bag and a chicken.
Player 4: I went to the market and bought an apricot, a bag, a chicken and a donkey.

Remembering everything that has gone before becomes more difficult as the game goes on. If you can't remember, or recite the list wrongly, you're out of that round. The last person left in the game is the winner.

TIP
If you try to picture each item in your head when it is mentioned, you can use that mental image to help you remember it.

139. CLIP THE CLIPS

2+ players
Use this easy trick to join two paperclips together without touching either one.

WHAT YOU WILL NEED:

- A banknote or a piece of paper in the shape of a banknote
- Two paperclips

WHAT YOU MUST DO:

The first thing to do is to show your audience the banknote so that they can see it is perfectly ordinary. If you can borrow the note from someone in the audience, that's even better.

Now fold the note in a loose zigzag so that you have three edges along the top as in diagram 1. Your paperclips now have to be slipped onto the note so that one is clipping the front of the note to the middle and the other is clipping the back of the note to the middle.

You can now announce that you will join the two clips together without touching either one. Grip each end of the banknote as shown in diagram 2.

Finally, you pull the note sharply open, so that it is entirely flat and unfolded. The paperclips will spring off the top of the note and, as if by magic, they will be neatly linked together.

1.

1. Place the clips to hold the note in a zigzag shape.

2.

2. With the clips in place, grip the ends of the note firmly.

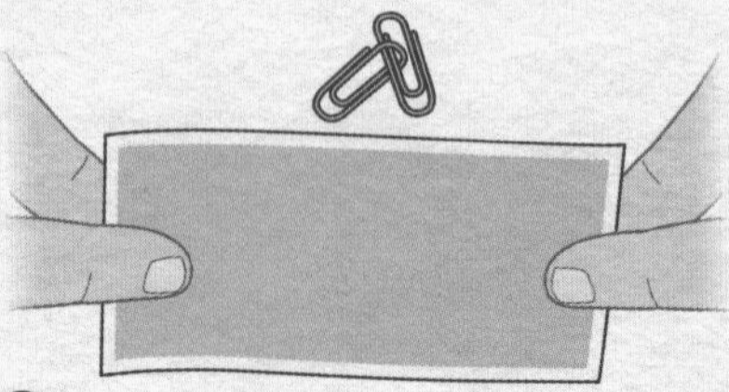

3.

3. Pull sharply open and the clips will ping off, locked together.

140. ANCIENT WONDER

I am as old as the world but new every month.

WHAT AM I?

Solution on page 218

141. CRASH MYSTERY

Two cars parked on the same single-track road one mile apart set off at the same time, traveling at 100 kph (60 mph), one heading east and one heading west. There was no room for them to pass or even for them to swerve to avoid each other, yet they did not crash into each other.

WHY?

Solution on page 218

142. JUMPING RUBBER BAND

2+ players
Make a rubber band jump across your hand.

WHAT YOU WILL NEED:

- A rubber band

WHAT YOU MUST DO:

This party trick looks really slick but it is actually very easy to master. Hold up one hand to your audience, turning it to show them the palm and the back of your hand so that they can see you are not hiding any kind of device or any other rubber bands.

With the back of your hand facing the audience, place a rubber band over your pinkie and ring finger. Keep the back of your hand to the audience and pull the band tight with your free hand, telling the audience that the band is tight, it's not broken and it can't slip off.

What you are actually doing is dragging the rubber band open into the palm of your hand. You then quickly curl your fingers into a clenched fist so that all of your fingertips are inside the band, then release the band as you unclench your fingers.

The rubber band will have jumped from your pinkie and ring finger to your middle and forefinger.

With a little practice, you can make the 'jump' happen very quickly and very smoothly so that, even if your audience is quite close, from their perspective looking at the back of your hand, they won't be able to tell how you did it.

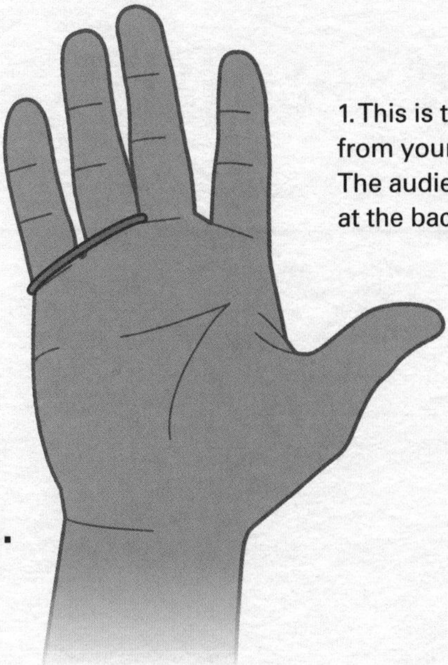

1.

1. This is the rubber band from your point of view. The audience will be looking at the back of your hand.

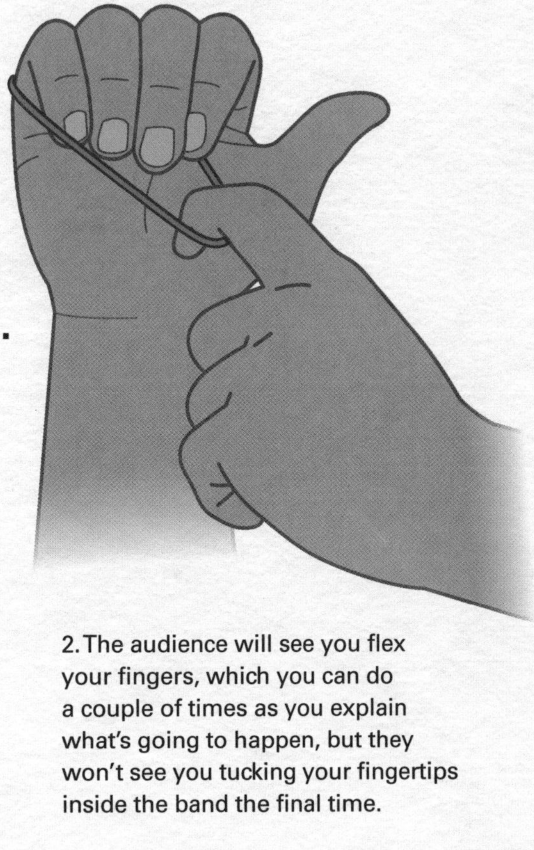

2.

2. The audience will see you flex your fingers, which you can do a couple of times as you explain what's going to happen, but they won't see you tucking your fingertips inside the band the final time.

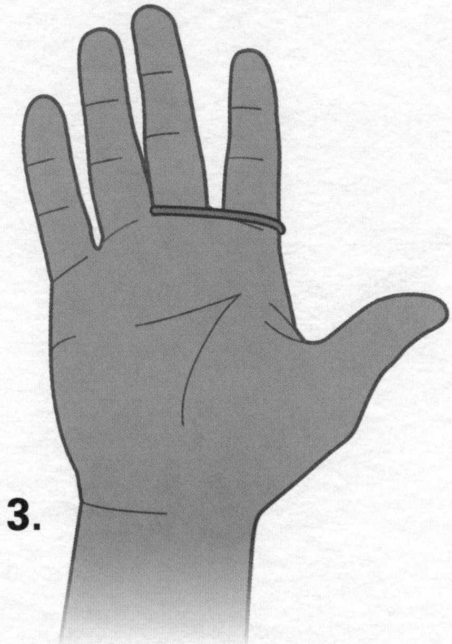

3.

3. When you throw your hand open, the rubber band will have magically 'jumped' to your other fingers.

TIP

The finger movements need to be snappy and fast for this trick to look slick, so you should practise it a few times to get it right.

143. BACKWARDS FISH

Can you move just three toothpicks to make this toothpick fish swim the other way?

Solution on page 218

144. IT'S ALL YOURS

What belongs to you but others use it more than you do?

HINT
Try to think about all the things that are yours, not just things you buy.

Solution on page 218

145. STAYING ALOFT

What is up with the birds and goes round above the trees all day without ever touching a leaf or landing on a branch or twig?

Solution on page 219

146. LEG LISTS

2+ players
How many things can you think of that have legs?

WHAT YOU WILL NEED:

- A sheet of paper
- A pencil
- Scissors

WHAT YOU MUST DO:

Write down the letters of the alphabet from A to Z and then cut them out so that you have 26 scraps of paper, each with a letter on it.

Turn the letters face down in the middle of a table and mix them all up.

The first player picks a letter from the pile and must name something beginning with that letter that has legs. If the first player picks the letter 'P', then he or she might say 'Panda'. The next player must also name something beginning with P that has legs – piano, pig, parrot, postman or pterodactyl are a few examples. The round continues with each person naming something beginning with P that has legs.

If a player can't come up with an answer, or gives an answer that has already been given, that player is out of the round. The winner of the round is the last player left and that player keeps the letter. He or she then chooses the next letter and the game begins again.

The player with the most letters at the end of the game is the winner.

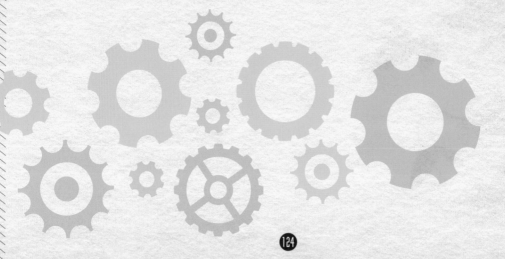

147. CHESS PROBLEM

How many squares are on a chessboard? If you think that the answer is 64, then think again!

Solution on page 219

148. COMBINATION CODES

2+ players
Come up with the longest word using a list of codes.

WHAT YOU WILL NEED:

- Pencils and paper for everyone
- A stopwatch
- A dictionary

WHAT YOU MUST DO:

Pass round a piece of paper on which every player must write down a combination of two letters – AU, RT, SM and so forth. Each player marks one combination and the sheet ends up looking like the sort of coded message a spy might have sent.

When all the combinations have been written, the first one is called out and everyone has one minute to think of the longest word they can that includes those letters in the order that they appear.

For AU, you could have 'faulty', 'Austria', 'laughter' or 'Australia'. Each player reads out his or her word in turn so that everyone can agree that the word is correct. If you have not come up with a correct word, you score no points. Disputed words should be checked in the dictionary. If you have thought of a correct word, you score one point for each letter.

In the case of AU, the player who wrote 'faulty' would score six, while the player who wrote 'Australia' would score nine.

Once you have been through all of the combination codes, add up your scores to see who has won that round, then come up with a new set of combinations to start again.

149. THE BODYGUARDS

A wealthy man employs two bodyguards and orders them never to let him out of their sight. The bodyguards develop an ingenious way of protecting their boss. One always faces west and the other always faces east. They use no mirrors or other reflections, so how can they both always keep their boss in their line of sight?

Solution on page 219

150. ALPHA RACE

2+ players
The clock is ticking and you have just 60 seconds to make your list.

WHAT YOU WILL NEED:

- A stopwatch
- Pencil and paper for everyone
- Scissors
- A dictionary

WHAT YOU MUST DO:

Write all of the letters of the alphabet on a piece of paper and cut them out individually. Put all the letters on a table face down and mix them up.

The first player then chooses a letter and shouts it out to everyone. The player in charge of timing then shouts 'Go!' and everyone has one minute to write down as many words as they can think of beginning with that letter.

After one minute, everyone must stop and pass their sheets to the right to be checked by the player sitting next to them. You score one point for each word.

Once marking is complete, the sheets are handed back and the next player picks out another letter. After 26 rounds – one for each letter of the alphabet – you add up your scores and the player with the most points wins.

To avoid arguments over whether a player's spelling is correct or if the word exists at all, look it up in the dictionary.

151. THE NAME GAME

2+ players
How would you describe yourself, in words using your initials?

WHAT YOU WILL NEED:

- A stopwatch
- Pencil and paper

WHAT YOU MUST DO:

This game is all about being able to think fast, using your imagination and letting your sense of humour shine through.

The first player has to think of a name of someone that everyone will recognize. It could be someone in the room, a famous personality, a family member or a friend that everyone knows.

The next player then has 30 seconds to think of two words to describe that person and the words must start with the person's initials. Paul Murphy, for example, might be 'powerful mind' or 'perfect moustache'.

If you come up with a description that fits or that makes people laugh within the time limit, you score a point.

One player should be in charge of keeping the time and another in charge of keeping everyone's scores. When you can no longer think of any famous names, the player with the highest score is the winner.

TIP
Don't panic when it comes to your turn – 30 seconds is plenty of time to think of a couple of words.

152. MENTAL ARITHMETIC

TRY this sum by working it out IN YOUR HEAD without using a pencil and paper or any kind of calculator. Take 1000 and add 40 to it. Now add another 1000 to it. Now add 30. And another 1000. Now add 20. Now add another 1000. Now add 10.

WHAT'S YOUR TOTAL?

Solution on page 219

153. LATE ARRIVAL?

What is always on its way but never actually gets here?

Solution on page 219

HINT
You might think the answer is travel-related, but think carefully, what else can be 'on its way'?

154. BOXES

2+ players
In this game, the winner comes last.

WHAT YOU WILL NEED:

- As many toothpicks as you can find

WHAT YOU MUST DO:

Create a grid of toothpick boxes, laying the toothpicks out horizontally and vertically to make as big a grid as you can. You should aim to have a grid at least five boxes wide and five boxes high – for that you will need 60 toothpicks.

Each player then takes a turn at picking up toothpicks from the grid. You can pick up one toothpick, or you can pick up two if they are touching.

The last player to pick up a toothpick is the winner.

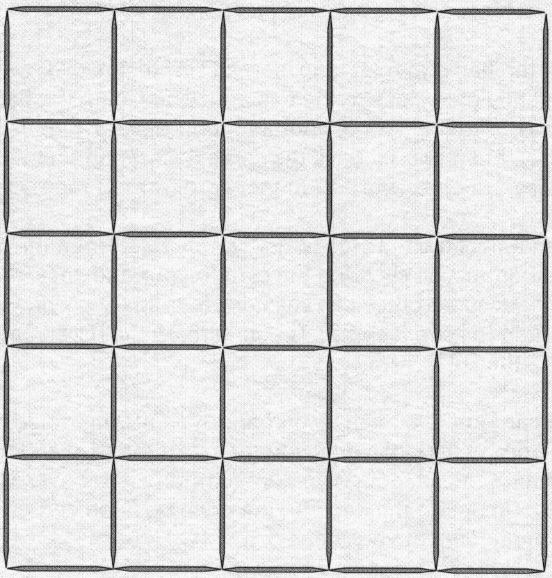

155. THE FLOATING CARD

2+ players
Make a playing card hover in mid-air above your hand!

WHAT YOU WILL NEED:

- Two playing cards
- A craft knife
- Some glue

WHAT YOU MUST DO:

Like so many magic tricks, to perform this one successfully you have to do your best to distract your audience. By talking to them constantly and keeping your hands on the move, you will give them no chance of spotting how you are making the card float above the palm of your hand.

You must also prepare very carefully for this trick to create your special floating card. You need to use a craft knife to cut a flap in the middle of a playing card. The card will stand on this flap when you are making it look like it is floating, so the flap needs to be long enough to hold the card clear of your hand, but not so long that it will be noticeable when you have it in the 'closed' position.

Once you have cut the flap and bent it up, spread some glue over the face of the card. Take care not to get any glue close to the flap area. Then, with the flap in the 'open' position, stick your card to the back of another identical card. It doesn't have to be the same suit or number, but it should have the same decoration on the back and be exactly the same size – in other words, another card from the same pack.

Leave the flap open and allow the glue to dry completely. When the glue is dry, you can close the flap and practise showing the card to your audience. You can show them the card front and back so that they can see it is an ordinary playing card. Hold a finger or thumb over the flap to keep it closed. The pattern on the back of most playing cards will help to disguise the cut lines.

Having shown the card to the audience, perhaps even having made it look as though you took it from a normal pack of cards, you then take the card and move it around over the palm of your hand as though you are tempting it to hover. What you are actually doing is manipulating the flap into the open position and gripping the very end of it between the fingers of your open palm.

You will have to practise how you show the card 'hovering'. It needs to be low down so that the audience can't see the flap. Keep your free hand on the move, swirling it around the card to distract the audience.

Finish the trick by snapping up the card with your free hand and secretly closing the flap before you give your audience another brief view of the card, front and back. Then put it away with the rest of the deck of cards before anyone can spot what makes your floating card so special.

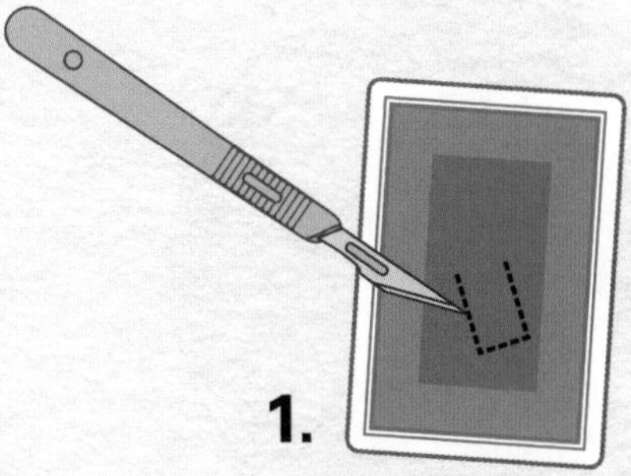

1.

2.

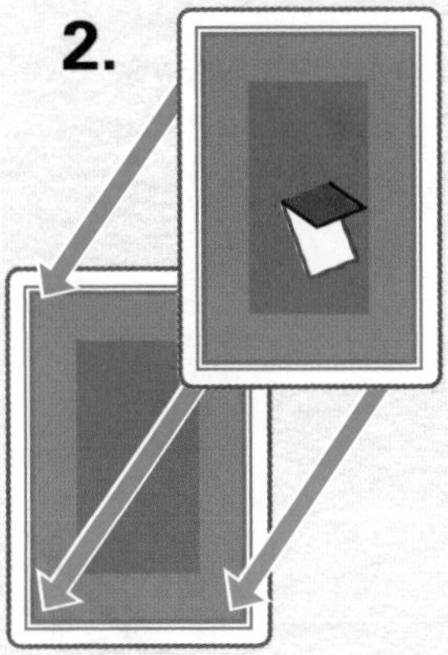

2. Stick the card to the back of another playing card that has an identical pattern on the back.

1. Use a craft knife to cut the flap and cut it at an angle so that the card will 'hover' at an angle over your hand.

3.

3. When you place the card in your flat palm, secretly open the flap and trap it between your fingers.

4.

4. Hold the card at an angle to your audience so that they can see it is 'floating' above your palm, but can't see the flap underneath.

TIP

When preparing this trick, make sure that there is no glue under the flap and that you keep the flap open until the glue is completely dry.

156. HIDE AND SEEK

Is it true when people say that when they lose something they always find it in the last place they would think of looking?

Solution on page 219

157. UPS AND DOWNS

This is something that will always go up but will never come down.

WHAT IS IT?

TIP

Don't get frustrated if you don't get the answer straight away. This riddle will take a little bit of lateral thinking to solve.

Solution on page 219

158. SON OF MY FATHER

A father and his young son are on a long train journey and the boy's father goes to the buffet car to buy them some sandwiches. He has their tickets in his wallet. While he is gone, a ticket inspector and a police officer come walking through the carriage. The boy has nothing to show them, but the police officer says to the ticket inspector, 'Don't worry, this boy is my son.'

HOW CAN THAT BE TRUE?

Solution on page 219

159. MINI WORDS

2+ players
Make as many small words as you can from one long word.

WHAT YOU WILL NEED:

- Pencil and paper for everyone
- A stopwatch

WHAT YOU MUST DO:

Each player takes it in turn to come up with a good, long word like POLITICIAN or INVESTIGATION.

The word is written on a piece of paper so that everyone agrees on the spelling, then everyone has two minutes to write down as many small words as they can, using only the letters in the big word.

You don't have to use all of the letters in the big word and you can use the same letters more than once, but not more than once in the same small word.

From POLITICIAN, for example, you could get:

CAN, TIP, CLAN, TIN, PLAN, LOT, PAN, TOIL,
TO, IT, LIT, CLAP, CAP, TAP, TAN, LIP,
LAP, NIT, PIT, NAP, TOP, POT, CLOT, PIN,
NIP, PICT, PACT, PAIN, PAINT, POINT

After two minutes, you swap sheets with the player next to you and take it in turns to read out each other's answers, marking one point for every correct word on the sheet and ten points if the player has come up with a word that uses all of the letters from the big word.

Once all the papers are marked and returned, start again with a new big word.

160. GIN RUMMY

2+ players
Collect matched sets and win points to become the champion.

WHAT YOU WILL NEED:

- A pack of cards
- Pencil and paper to keep score

WHAT YOU MUST DO:

Each player is dealt ten cards. The object is to collect sets of three or four cards. Sets can be cards of the same value or cards of the same suit running in sequence (three, four, five and six of diamonds, for instance).

The remaining cards are placed in a stack in the middle, face down. The top card is turned over and placed face up to start the discard pile. The player who did not deal begins by picking up either the card off the discard pile or one off the top of the stack. He or she must then choose which card to discard as you can only have ten in your hand.

If you collect a 'gin hand' – say, two sets of three and a set of four – you knock on the table to end the game as you discard your last card. You can knock earlier, if you have a couple of good sets and some low-ranked, unmatched cards.

You get 25 points for a gin hand plus the value of your opponent's unmatched cards. Ace counts as 1 and face cards as 10. If you knock without a gin hand and your opponent has a higher value of unmatched cards than you do, the difference is the number of points you score.

161. LOVE AND MARRIAGE

He has married many women but he has never had a wife.

WHO IS HE?

Solution on page 219

162. UNTOUCHABLE

You can see me but not touch me.
Put me in a bucket and I will make it lighter.

WHAT AM I?

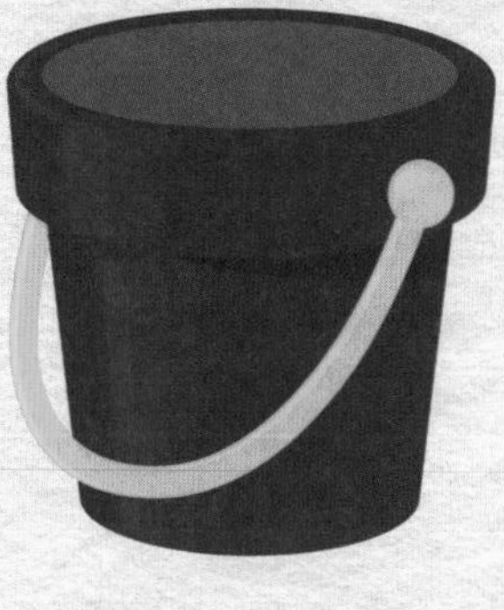

Solution on page 219

163. IMPOSSIBLE PAPER

2+ players
Turn a sheet of paper into a shape that can't possibly exist!

WHAT YOU WILL NEED:

- One sheet of A4 paper
- A pair of scissors

WHAT YOU MUST DO:

Take a look at the piece of paper in the first diagram. There is a single flap sticking up in the middle and a slot on either side, but the flap can't possibly have come from either of the slots. It's not an optical illusion or a trick drawing. You can actually make this seemingly impossible piece of paper – but if you challenge anyone else to do it, they won't know where to start.

To begin with, you need to fold your paper to mark eight equal segments. Fold it in half lengthwise, then open it out. Fold it in half the other way, then in half again and open it out so that you now have eight segments marked on your sheet.

On one side, make two cuts from the edge into the middle, separating the end segments from the middle two. On the other side, make one cut from the edge to the middle, cutting this side of the paper exactly in half.

You now have two cuts on one side of the paper and one cut on the other. You must now flip one half of the sheet as shown in illustration 3, then lay the sheet flat on the table in front of you.

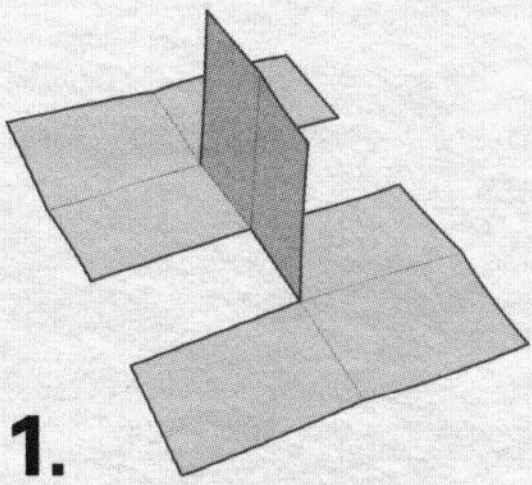

1.

1. This paper shape looks like it is impossible to create from one sheet.

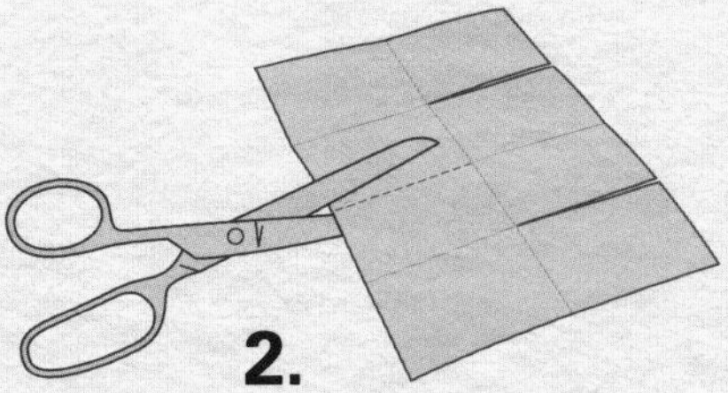

2.

2. Cut accurately along the fold lines only as far as the middle.

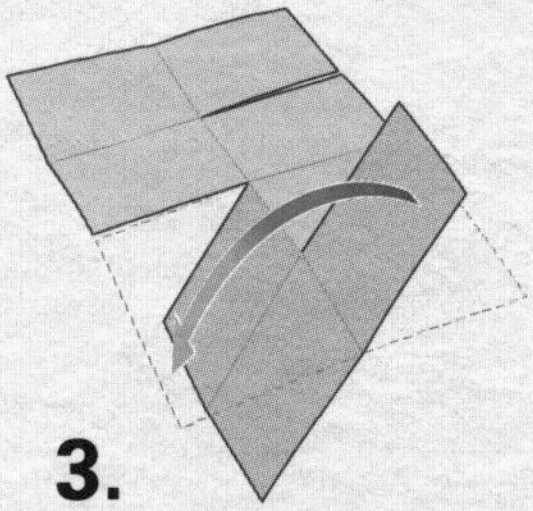

3.

3. Flip one side to create the shape that looks like it's impossible.

164. HOT AND COLD

2+ players
Younger children love this game because it gets very noisy!

WHAT YOU WILL NEED:

- A small object to hide – sweets are good because you can eat them when you find them.

WHAT YOU MUST DO:

One player is sent out of the room and the others choose a hiding place for the object. When they have hidden it, they all call out 'Come and find it!' and the player comes back into the room.

The player then makes his way around the room, looking for the hidden object. The others help by calling out 'Cold!' if the seeker is far away from the object, 'Colder!' if the seeker moves farther away, or 'Freezing!' if the player is still going wrong.

On the other hand, if the player is getting close, the others call out 'Warm!', 'Warmer!', 'Hot!' or 'Scorching!'

When the object is found, another player is chosen to step outside and the game begins again.

TIP
Have fun when calling out directions by using as many different 'hot' and 'cold' words as you can, like 'Toasty!' and 'Sunburned!' or 'Arctic!' and 'Snowman!'

165. THE CASTLE GUARD

In a land where three kings were at war over who owned some territory that bordered each of their kingdoms, a guard on night duty in the castle of one of the kings had a strange dream in which he saw the armies of the other two kings attacking at dawn.

He went to his king and told him that, in his dream, he had seen the armies of the other kings coming from the east as the sun rose. The king ordered his army to prepare to defend the castle. At dawn, just as the guard had said, the enemy forces appeared. Because the army had set up its defences, the attackers were repelled and everyone in the castle was saved.

The king then demanded to see the guard who had told him of the attack and had him thrown into the dungeon.

WHY DID HE DO THIS?

Solution on page 219

166. MIXED MESSAGES

2+ players
Create a silly message using the letters in a chosen word.

WHAT YOU WILL NEED:

- A pencil and paper

WHAT YOU MUST DO:

Each player takes it in turn to think of a key word and write it down. The player to the left of the one who has written the word then starts the message by saying a word that begins with the first letter of the key word. The next player says a word beginning with the second letter, and so on.

For example, if the key word is TELEVISION:

Player 1	**T**iny
Player 2	**E**lephants
Player 3	**L**ike
Player 4	**E**ating
Player 5	**V**egetables
Player 6	**I**n
Player 7	**S**ocks
Player 8	**I**roned
Player 9	**O**ver
Player 10	**N**achos

Of course, you don't need ten players, you just keep taking turns until you have used up all the letters in the word. The player who wrote the first word has to write down each new word and then read the message. Try to make it as silly as possible to give everyone a laugh!

After reading the message, move on to the next player's key word.

167. FLOATING PENCIL

2+ players
Make a pencil move up and down inside an empty bottle.

WHAT YOU WILL NEED:

- A bottle (preferably with dark glass)
- A pencil
- A piece of thread

WHAT YOU MUST DO:

This is another trick that you must prepare in advance and be able to set up quickly simply by turning your back to the audience, making it look like you are picking the bottle up from a table behind you.

Hold the bottle in your left hand in front of you, and use your right hand to make lots of conjuring moves, waving it around the bottle to tempt the pencil out. The pencil will rise and start to climb out of the top of the bottle, then sink back down again on your command.

What the audience can't see is that there is a thread tied around the bottom of the pencil. In the illustration shown here, the bottle is clear and the thread is obvious, but with a darker bottle, especially if you are wearing a dark shirt, the thread will be very difficult to spot. The illustration shows a side view of how the trick works. Your audience will see it with you facing them, again making the thread hard to see.

The other end of the thread needs to be wound round a button on the front of your shirt, or your belt buckle, whichever is easiest for you to do quickly with your back to the audience when you first pick up the bottle. Then you can make the pencil rise by pushing your left hand away from your body, and make it fall to the bottom again by bringing your hand closer to your body.

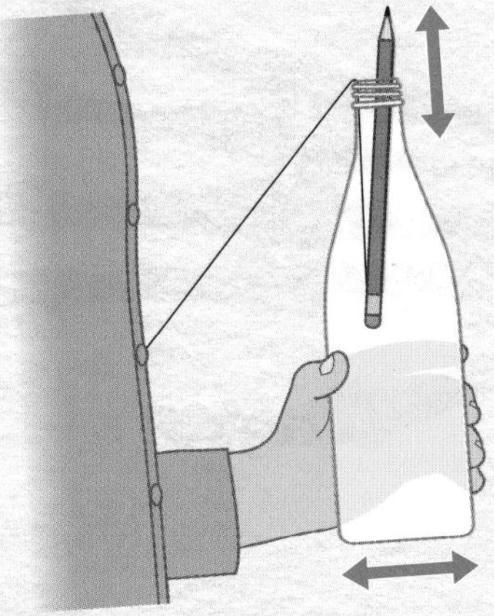

TIP
From the side, it is clear how the trick works but from the front, where the audience is, it is a mystery.

168. SOMETHING TO BE KEPT

What can you only keep after you have first given it to someone else?

Solution on page 219

169. GRIPPING PROBLEM

They have no flesh, they have no bone, yet they have fingers and thumbs of their own.

WHAT ARE THEY?

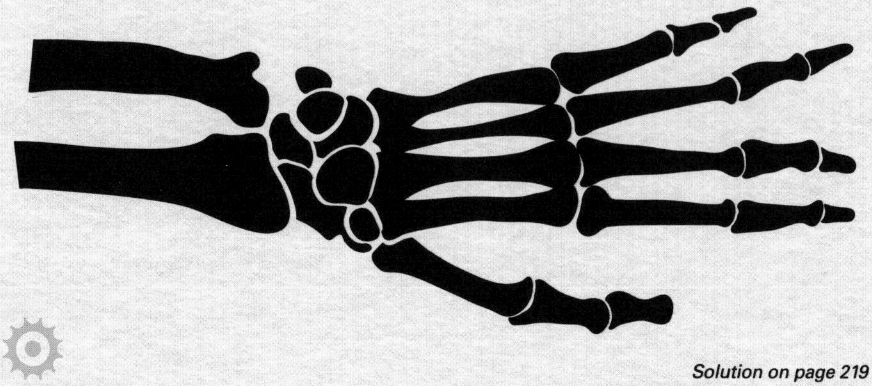

Solution on page 219

170. MURDER IN THE DARK

5+ players
Can the detective uncover the evil villain before another murder is committed?

WHAT YOU WILL NEED:

- A pack of cards

WHAT YOU MUST DO:

Count out one card for each player, including the ace of diamonds and the ace of spades. Give one card to each player.

The player who gets the ace of diamonds is the detective and the only one who can reveal his card. The player who gets the ace of spades is the murderer and must keep it a secret. The detective then leaves the room and the lights are switched off so that people are moving around in complete darkness.

The murderer taps a victim three times on the shoulder. The victim screams and falls to the floor. Everyone freezes except the murderer who can move away. The detective waits ten seconds, then enters and switches on the light. He then questions witnesses, asking them if they felt anyone moving around, or who they think the murderer is. He can ask six questions.

Everyone must tell the truth, except the murderer. The detective can ask anyone 'Are you the murderer?', but can only ask this once. If the person is not the murderer, the detective has lost. The cards are then dealt again to start a new game.

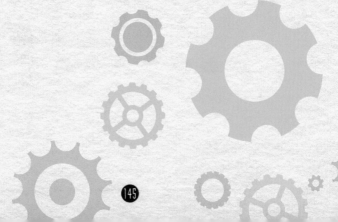

171. EIGHTS-A-GO-GO

2+ players
In this game you win by losing all your cards.

WHAT YOU WILL NEED:

- A pack of cards
- Pencil and paper

WHAT YOU MUST DO:

The dealer deals five cards to each player. The rest are placed in a stack, face down, and the top card is turned over to start a 'matching card' pile. If this card is an 8 it must be put back in the middle of the deck and the top card turned over again.

The aim is to discard all of your cards, one at a time, onto the matching cards pile. The player to the dealer's left begins. You have to be able to match the number or the suit of the card on top of the matching cards pile. If you don't have a matching card to discard, you have to take a card off the top of the deck.

If you have an 8, you can play it at any time and ask for the suit to be changed to whatever you want. For instance, if you have a lot of spades in your hand, you should choose spades.

The winner is the first person to discard all of their cards.

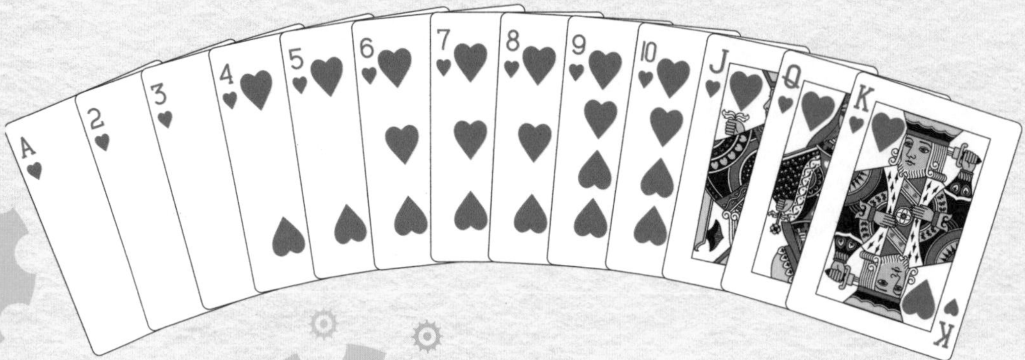

172. CATCH ME?

You can catch me
but not throw me.

WHAT AM I?

Solution on page 219

173. FIND MY HOME

I come in different shapes and sizes. Parts of me are curved, other parts are straight. You can keep me anywhere you like, but there is only one place where you need me to be.

WHAT AM I?

Solution on page 219

174. STRANGE SCENE

While walking past a house you spot a strange collection of things on the ground – nine lumps of coal, a carrot, a scarf and two broken twigs.

WHO DO YOU THINK LEFT THEM THERE?

Solution on page 219

175. HOLD ON

What is light as a feather but cannot be held for ten minutes by even the strongest of men?

HINT

The key word in this riddle is 'held'. Make a mental list of the various things that you can hold.

Solution on page 220

176. THE LOSER WINS

A very wealthy Arab sheikh was growing old and knew that he did not have many years left to live. He had two sons who argued with each other over everything. The old sheikh knew that his sons would argue over his money after he was dead, so he decided that he must put one of them in charge. The son who was put in charge would have to promise to split the old sheikh's wealth evenly with his brother.

The sons had identical Ferrari sports cars, so to decide who should be in charge after his death, the old sheikh set them a challenge. They had to race to a town many miles away, but the winner would be the one whose car took longest to reach the town.

The brothers were stumped. How could they stage a race where you had to go slowest to win? For once, they agreed on something – they needed help to figure out this problem. They drove their Ferraris to a tent where a wise man lived. After they had explained their problem, the wise man gave them some advice, whereupon the brothers rushed from the tent and sped off in the Ferraris towards the distant town.

WHAT DID THE WISE MAN TELL THEM TO DO?

Solution on page 220

177. REVERSE CARD

2+ players
The hidden card magically reveals itself by turning over in the deck.

WHAT YOU WILL NEED:

- A pack of cards

WHAT YOU MUST DO:

Prepare the pack by holding the deck of cards face down, then take the bottom card and turn it over so that it is face up. Return it to the bottom of the deck. The bottom card is now face up but no one can see it. You are now ready to face your audience.

Hold the cards spread out in a fan, face down, with the bottom (face up) card hidden at the end of the fan. Ask your volunteer to choose a card from the fan, but not to show it to you.

While the volunteer studies the chosen card, close the fan into a deck and, while distracting attention by talking, turn the deck over so that the bottom card is now on top. This card will now be face down while all the others are face up, although no one can see them in the closed deck.

Have the volunteer hide the chosen card by slipping it into the deck somewhere in the middle. The volunteer will be putting the card in face down, amongst a deck that is now secretly face up.

Put your hands behind your back, say a magic word and flip the top card while no one can see you doing it. You can now fan the cards out again, holding the pack face down, and the chosen card will appear somewhere near the middle of the fan face up!

178. IT BEGINS WITH...

3+ players
Think of as many names as you can beginning with the key letter.

WHAT YOU WILL NEED:

- A newspaper or magazine
- Pencils and paper for everyone
- A stopwatch

WHAT YOU MUST DO:

One of the players acts as the judge. The judge keeps the score, selects the topic and chooses the key letter.

You can decide together on a list of topics such as singers, film stars, football players, artists, presidents, animals, foods... you can make the list as long as you like. The judge chooses a topic from the list, then waves his or her pencil over a newspaper and jabs it down to select a random key letter.

Everyone must now think of as many names or words as they can from the chosen topic beginning with the key letter and write them down. For people you can use first or second names.

After two minutes, the judge calls 'Stop' and counts up everyone's answers, awarding a point for each correct name or word on their lists. Another player can then become judge for the next round.

179. SELF-SLICING BANANA

2+ players
Peel a banana to reveal that it is already sliced inside.

WHAT YOU WILL NEED:

- A fresh banana
- A long pin

WHAT YOU MUST DO:

Amaze your friends with this party trick, having first done just a little preparation. Offer to share a banana with someone, telling them, 'Don't worry, this banana comes pre-sliced.' When you peel it – or you let your friend peel it – the banana will indeed be cut into slices inside its skin.

For the trick to work, the banana obviously has to look like no one has tampered with it. There should be no trace of any cut marks on the skin and the banana will not have been peeled already.

To achieve the magically sliced banana effect, you need to use a long pin – an ordinary pin of the sort that you might find in a sewing kit. There are ridges on the skin of a banana and as the banana ripens these can take on a darker, brown colour.

Push the pin into the banana through one of the ridges, preferably at a dark spot. Move the pin from side to side as you push it in so that the pin under the skin gradually cuts through the banana.

Feel for when the pin inside the banana touches the inside of the banana skin to the left or right or at the other side of the banana, as you do not want to risk puncturing the skin.

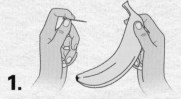

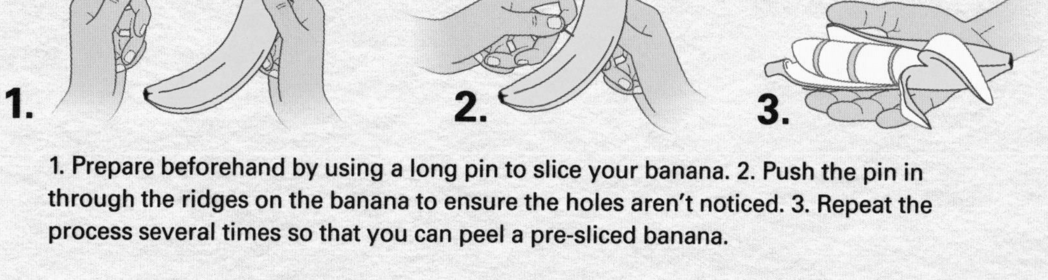

1. Prepare beforehand by using a long pin to slice your banana. 2. Push the pin in through the ridges on the banana to ensure the holes aren't noticed. 3. Repeat the process several times so that you can peel a pre-sliced banana.

180. FAST OR SLOW

Which can outrun you – cold or warmth?

Solution on page 220

181. GLOBETROTTER

What can travel the world while stuck in a corner?

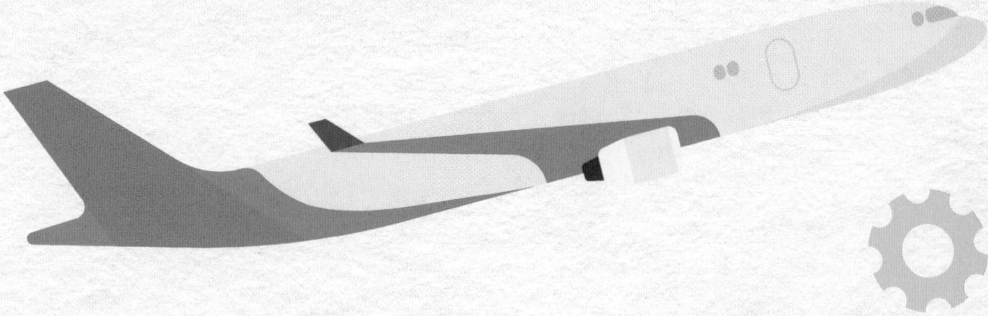

Solution on page 220

HINT

You may get a little 'stuck' yourself on this riddle, but what other sorts of thing can be stuck?

182. WORD LINKS

2+ players
Quick thinking is required to build a long chain of linked words.

WHAT YOU MUST DO:

One player starts by saying a word. The next player has to call out a word that is linked to that word or associated with it in some way. A typical linked chain might go as follows:

Player 1: Ball
Player 2: Foot
Player 3: Sock
Player 4: Smelly
Player 5: Uncle

At this point one of the other players might call 'Challenge' because they see no obvious link between 'Smelly' and 'Uncle'. Player 5 can say that he has an uncle who works in a cheese shop and it's really smelly.

Everyone else must decide whether that is an acceptable link. If it's not, then Player 5 drops out of the game. If it is, then whoever called 'Challenge' is out of the game.

The last player left is the winner.

TIP
Think fast but try not to suggest links that only you can really understand because others might not be prepared to accept them.

183. 65 SQUARE

The numbers 1 up to 25 must be placed in the circles of the square below in such a way that the sum of the numbers in each row, column and diagonal amounts to 65.

HOW SHOULD THE NUMBERS BE ARRANGED IN THE SQUARE?

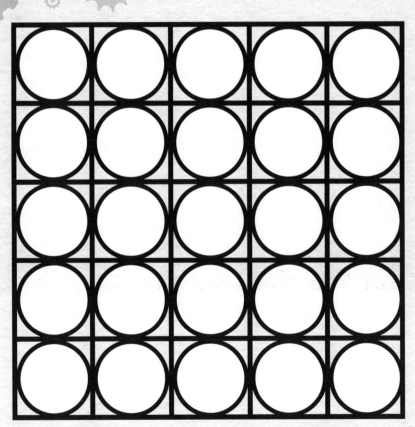

Solution on page 220

184. MAKE A CENTURY

Below is an equation that is not correct yet. By adding a number of plus signs and minus signs between the digits on the left side (without changing the order of the digits), the equation can be made correct.

123456789 = 100

HOW MANY WAYS CAN YOU COME UP WITH TO MAKE 100?

Solution on page 220

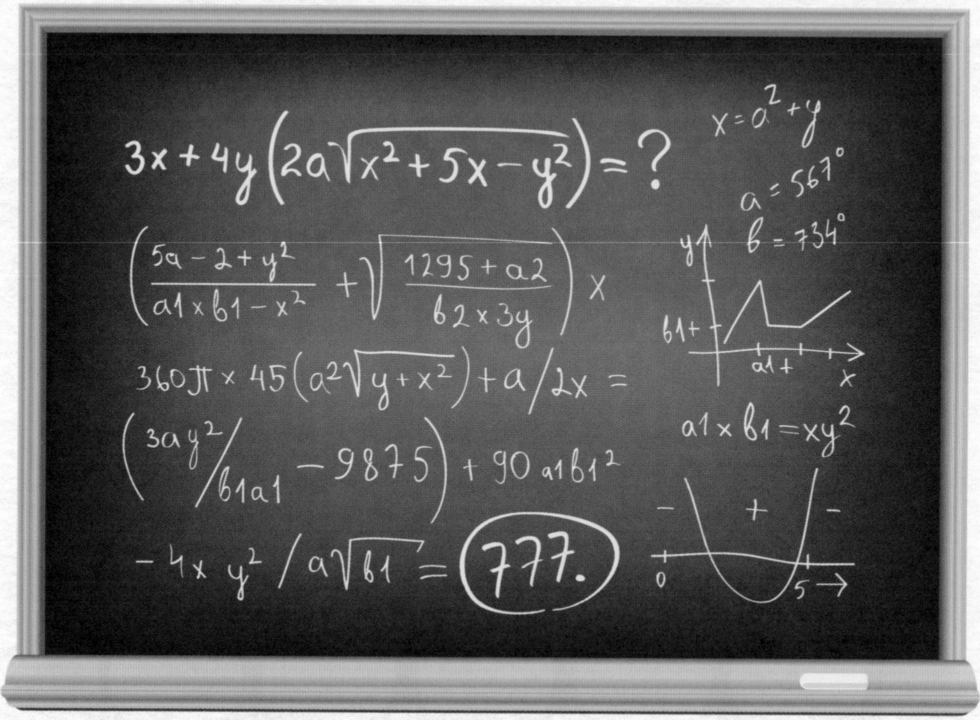

185. MONEY MATTERS

2+ players
This trick uses two banknotes and what matters is which one comes out on top.

WHAT YOU WILL NEED:

- Two banknotes or two pieces of paper roughly the same size as banknotes.

WHAT YOU MUST DO:

Make sure that the banknotes are different or that the pieces of paper are different colours. If your two notes look identical, it will be difficult to understand at the end of the trick that they have somehow changed places.

Position the two notes as shown in the first illustration. They should form a 'V' pointing towards you but the top note should be clear of the edges of the note below, especially at the bottom where they are closest to you.

Start to roll the notes up, rolling both together. Keep it as neat as you can and carry on rolling the notes until you get to the end of the bottom note. At this point there will still be some of the top note left to roll up. As you roll on, the tip of the note that was on the bottom will flip over the roll. Put a finger on it, without making it obvious you are doing so, stop rolling and start to unroll the notes again. You can release your finger once you have started to carefully unroll the notes towards you.

When you finish unrolling the notes, the one that was on the bottom – in the illustrations here it is the brown note – will now be on top!

1.
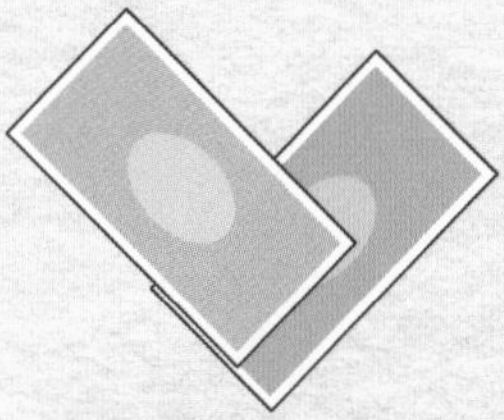

1. The top of the top note should be farthest away from you.

2.
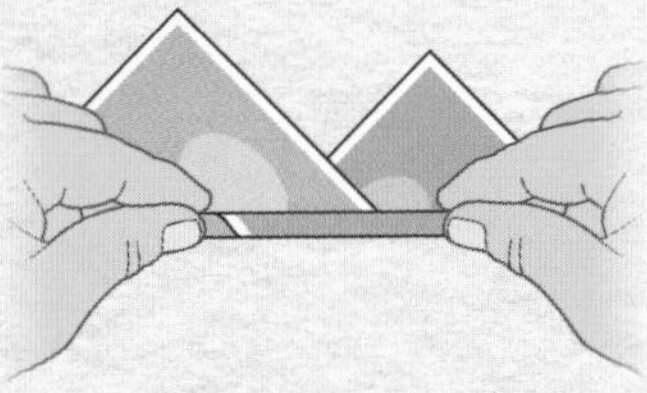

2. Roll them until the top of the bottom note flips over.

3.
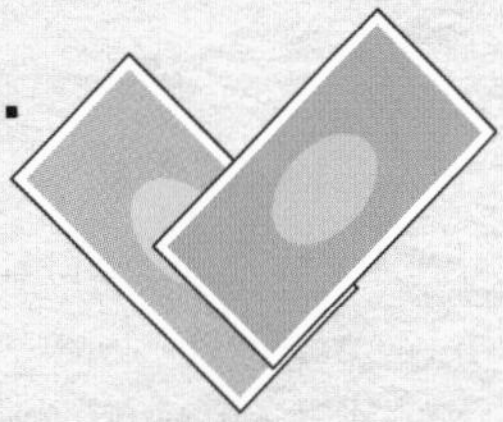

3. Unroll them and they've changed places.

186. TUMBLING EGGS

2+ players
The challenge is to flip an egg without actually touching it at all.

WHAT YOU WILL NEED:

- A raw egg
- A shot glass (small drinks glass used for spirits)

WHAT YOU MUST DO:

Put the egg in the shot glass with the wider end of the egg sitting inside the glass. Your challenge is to turn the egg upside down without touching the egg or the glass.

The way to do it is to lean over the egg so that you are directly over the very top of the shell and then blow down on the egg. Try it gently at first, but when you blow with just the right strength, the egg will miraculously jump up in the air and turn over.

To impress your audience, you can then crack the egg into a bowl or a larger glass to show them that you weren't using any sort of a trick egg.

Lean over the egg so that you can blow down directly onto the point to make the egg do a somersault.

187. TAKE IT AWAY

The more you take away from me, the bigger I will grow.

WHAT AM I?

Solution on page 220

188. VANISHING HEAD

What loses its head in the morning but gets it back again

IN THE EVENING?

Solution on page 220

189. SHROUD OF MYSTERY

2+ players
Use the Shroud of Mystery to make a coin disappear into thin air.

WHAT YOU WILL NEED:

- A cloth or napkin to serve as your Shroud of Mystery
- An ordinary coin

WHAT YOU MUST DO:

Explain to your audience that your Shroud of Mystery has magic properties and can make a coin vanish from your hand. It is important that, while you are talking to your audience, you move your Shroud of Mystery around, draping it over your hand and generally making your audience pay attention to the cloth, whether they know that they are doing so or not.

Hold the cloth clasped between your forefinger and middle finger. This looks quite casual and allows you to drape the cloth over either hand as you move it about. The purpose of the cloth, after all, is to conceal what you will be doing.

Pick up a coin and hold it in your other hand. Balance it on top of your closed fist and then show the coin in the palm of your hand before you close your hand around it and hold up your closed fist again, this time with the coin held tightly inside.

Pass the Shroud of Mystery over your closed fist a couple of times and tell the audience that you can still feel the coin in your hand until, with one final flourish, you run the cloth over your hand, dragging it from behind your fist, over the top and down in front. The instant that the cloth is hiding your fist from the audience, let the coin drop from your fist into the open palm of your other hand.

At that point, you can announce that you no longer feel the coin in your hand, open your fist and show everyone that the Shroud of Mystery has made the coin disappear.

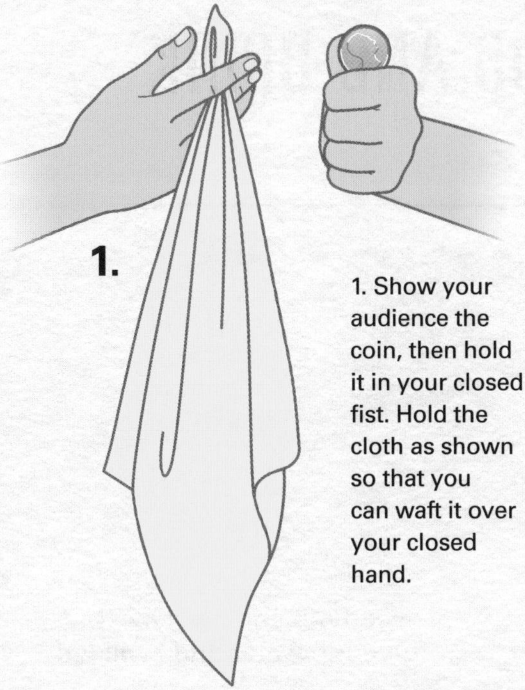

1.

1. Show your audience the coin, then hold it in your closed fist. Hold the cloth as shown so that you can waft it over your closed hand.

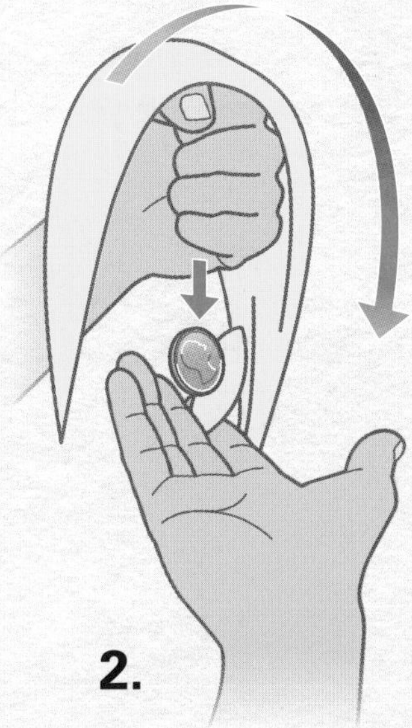

2.

2. Pass the cloth over your hand a few times while talking to the audience then, on a final pass, drop the coin from one hand into the other.

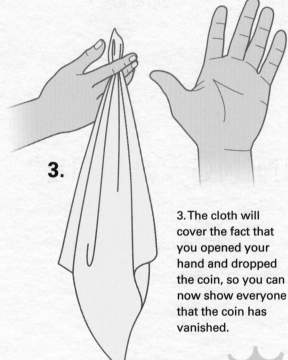

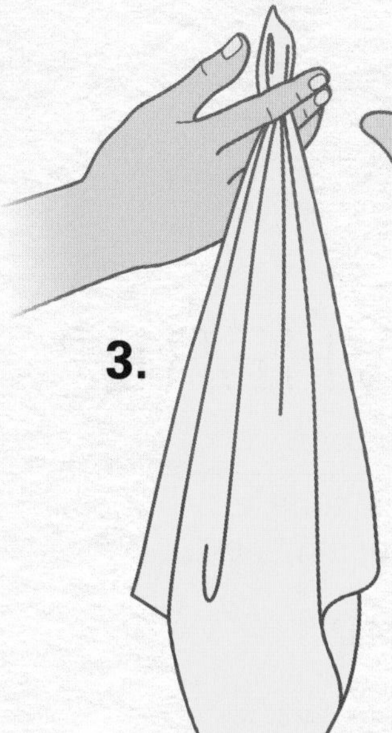

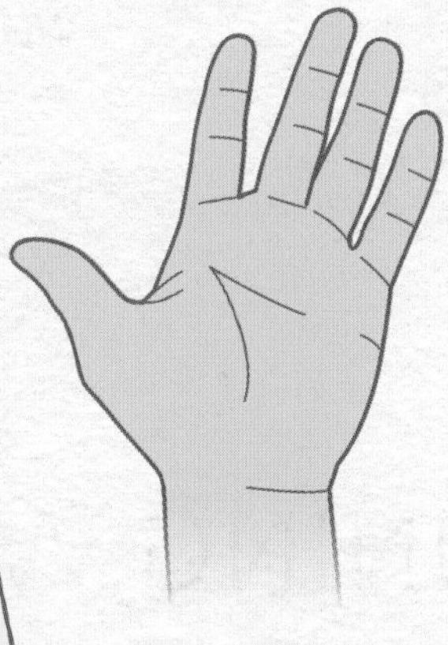

3.

3. The cloth will cover the fact that you opened your hand and dropped the coin, so you can now show everyone that the coin has vanished.

TIP

You need to use the Shroud of Mystery to cover what you are doing with your hands and, as in all magic tricks, practice makes perfect.

190. FOOD AND DRINK

Feed me and I will live but give me water and I will die.

WHAT AM I?

Solution on page 220

191. RUNNING WHERE?

Split in two, just in time,
standing still I'm running fine.

WHAT AM I?

TIP
This is a rhyming riddle, which should make it easier to remember if you need to think about it later.

Solution on page 221

192. BEHIND YOU

Susan is standing behind Helen at the same time as Helen is standing behind Susan.

HOW IS THIS POSSIBLE?

Solution on page 221

193. TAKE IT AWAY

How many times can
you subtract **10 FROM 100?**

Solution on page 221

194. HEADS AND FEET

A farmer has chickens roaming around a field where cows are grazing. He tries to count them. He counts 8 heads and 28 feet.

HOW MANY COWS DOES HE HAVE AND HOW MANY CHICKENS?

Solution on page 221

195. FATHERS AND SONS

A man joins a small group looking at a portrait. He studies the portrait for a moment and then says, "Brothers and sisters I have none, but that man's father is my father's son."

WHO IS IN THE PORTRAIT?

Solution on page 221

196. PARADISE ISLAND

Three sailors on a yacht approached a tropical island and spotted a beautiful beach where they decided to spend a while lazing in the sunshine. They all dived into the water head first to swim ashore. None of them was wearing any kind of hat or swimming cap and all of them went under the water before bobbing up to start swimming, but only two of them got their hair wet.

HOW COULD THIS BE?

Solution on page 221

197. NINE TRIANGLES

By adding 3 straight lines, make the M into 9 triangles.

Solution on page 221

198. MIND READING

4+ players
Amaze your friends with your ability to read minds!

WHAT YOU WILL NEED:

- An accomplice

WHAT YOU MUST DO:

Secretly plan this trick in advance with an accomplice. No one must know you are working together. Gather your friends around a table and tell them that you can read minds. Place an object in the middle of the table – a book would do – then leave the room.

Someone in the room must pick up the book and it will be your job to say who it was by reading their minds. When you come back into the room, pick up the book, concentrate, then announce who it was that touched it.

How did you know? Your accomplice told you. You need to arrange a code with your accomplice. When you come back into the room, your accomplice should be sitting with his or her hands on the table or with their arms folded.
If their hands are on the table with two fingers of the right hand extended, it means that the person sitting two places to the right was the one who touched the book. You can use the same signal technique with the left hand or, with the arms folded, where the hand showing on the left or right displays the finger code.

As long as no one spots you checking the code, you will look like a mind reader!

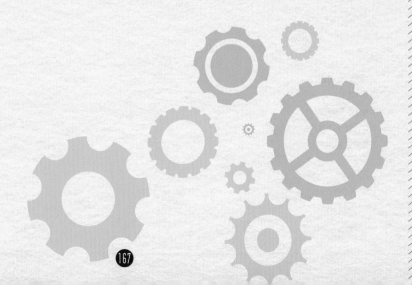

199. FLYING PENCIL

2+ players
You will struggle to keep control of this amazing pencil as it soars towards the ceiling!

WHAT YOU WILL NEED:

- A pencil

WHAT YOU MUST DO:

Lay the pencil on the table, pick it up, wave it around and talk about how, with a little concentration, you can make it rise towards the ceiling.

Grip the pencil in a closed fist with the back of your hand facing upwards. Use the magic word 'Ascendium' and let your hand drift higher as though the pencil is pushing it up. Grip your wrist with your free hand to stop it going any higher.

At this point you can open your fingers and say to everyone, 'Look – I'm not holding on to it. It's pushing my hand upwards!' and it will look like the pencil is, indeed, pushing against your hand.

What you have actually done, without anyone being able to see, is to extend the forefinger of the hand that is gripping your wrist and use it to hold the pencil in place.

Use the magic word, 'Descendium' and slowly lower the pencil back down towards the table, releasing your forefinger when it is near the tabletop and letting your wrist go.

1. Use one hand to try to hold down your rising wrist.

2. Secretly hold on to the pencil.

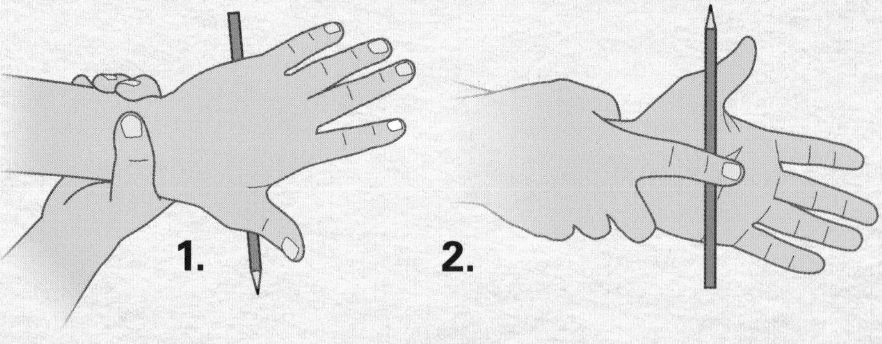

200. BRICK BUILDING

On a building site, 80 bricklayers lay 80,000 bricks in eight days. How many bricks do 40 bricklayers lay in **4 DAYS?**

Solution on page 221

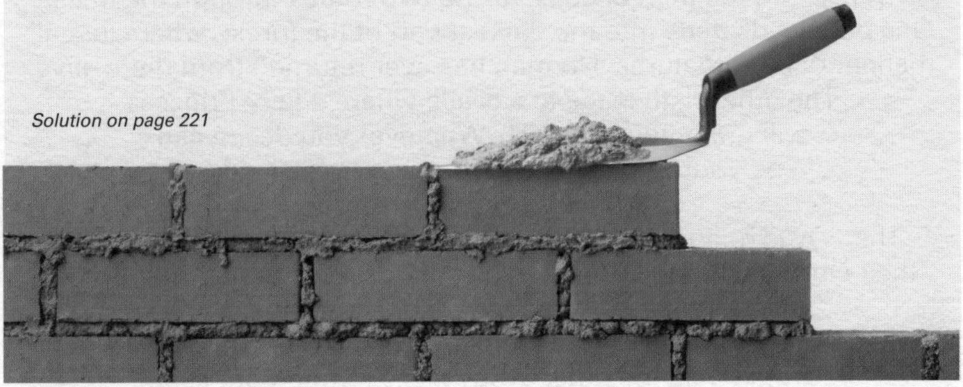

201. FALL GUY

A man painting window frames on the top floor of his house slips and falls, yet he is completely unhurt.

WHY WAS HE NOT INJURED?

Solution on page 221

202. THE GIANT AND THE TROLL

A traveller is hiking through an enchanted forest when he meets an old woman who warns him to turn back. When he asks why, she says, 'Ahead the path divides, taking two routes through the trees. One path leads deep into the darkest part of the forest, where lurk all manner of evil creatures. No man has ever returned from there alive. The other path leads to a castle where a fairy princess will grant you one wish. Whatever you desire can be yours – wealth, wisdom or everlasting life.

'The way is guarded by a giant and a troll. Once they have you in their clutches, they will force you to choose one path. You may ask one question to either the giant or the troll, but be warned, one of them is sworn always to tell the truth while the other always tells nothing but lies.'

'Excellent!' says the traveller. 'Then I shall look forward to meeting the fairy princess!' And he sets off up the path. What question did the traveller intend to ask, and who did he ask – the giant or the troll?

Solution on page 221

TIP

There are lots of characters and details in this story, but don't let them distract you. The answer is probably simpler than you think. Just concentrate on finding the 'truth'.

203. CROSSWORDS

2+ players
Be the first one to finish your crossword with the most words.

WHAT YOU WILL NEED:

- Paper for each player
- Pencils for each player

WHAT YOU MUST DO:

Each player draws a grid on their paper six boxes wide by six boxes deep – you can make the grids bigger if you want the game to go on longer.

Players then take it in turns to call out a letter of the alphabet and everyone must mark that letter somewhere on their grid.

The aim is to create words running horizontally or vertically on the grid. Words on one line or running directly above or below each other must be separated by shaded squares so that they don't touch, but vertical words can intersect horizontal words.

Think carefully where you put the letters that are called out so that you can construct words, leaving spaces while you wait for the letters that you need to be called. Letters can be called more than once.

Once you have filled up your grid, you drop out of the game and do not call letters. When there is just one person left calling, the game is over and the one with the most words on their grid is the winner. You can add numbers to your finished grid to make it look like a completed crossword.

204. SECRET FOURS

4+ players
Collect the most sets of four to win.

WHAT YOU WILL NEED:

- A pack of cards

WHAT YOU MUST DO:

Each player is dealt five cards and the rest are put in a stack in the middle of the table. They study their cards, then the player to the left of the dealer begins.

The first player asks any other player for specific cards. If, for example, you had two tens in your hand, you would ask the other player, 'Do you have any tens?' You must have at least one ten in your hand to ask for tens. If the player has any tens, they have to hand them over.

The first player can then continue by asking any other player either for tens or any other card. When he is refused, he picks up a card from the stack and play passes to the next player.

The object is to collect cards of the same rank, four sevens, four tens, four queens. When you have a set, you place it face up on the table in front of you. The player who collects the most sets by the time all of the cards are used up is the winner.

TIP
Remember what other players ask for so that you know what they are collecting, then ask them for the same thing if you can.

205. TABOO

2+ players
Answer The Inquisitor's questions without using the forbidden word.

WHAT YOU MUST DO:

One of the players is chosen as The Inquisitor. The Inquisitor declares a certain word or words to be taboo. Start off with just one or two taboo words, but make them frequently used words like 'the' or 'and'.

Taboo words must not be used when answering The Inquisitor's questions.

The Inquisitor then asks the first player a question, which can be anything, such as 'What did you do on Sunday?' or 'Describe the outside of your house.'
The player must answer without using any taboo words.

If anyone hears a taboo word being used, they have to yell 'TABOO!' and the player who used the forbidden word is out of the game.

The last player left in is the winner and becomes The Inquisitor for the next round.

206. LOSING YOUR BOTTLE

2+ players
Balance a bottle upside down on top of a banknote and challenge your friends to take the note without touching or tipping the bottle.

WHAT YOU WILL NEED:

- A banknote
- An empty bottle (a glass bottle works best as it is heavier)

WHAT YOU MUST DO:

Lay the banknote flat on a table and stand the bottle on top of it, balanced on its open end. The challenge is to get the banknote out from under the bottle without tipping it over.

The temptation for most people is to try to whip the note out quickly, like when you sometimes see a stage magician whipping a tablecloth out from beneath crockery laid on the table. That is very unlikely ever to work.

What you have to do is to treat the banknote and the bottle very gently. Roll the banknote from one edge until it reaches the bottle, then roll it even more carefully as it nestles up against the bottle.

Rolling the note will push the bottle at the same time as dragging the rest of the note out from underneath. If you are very careful, you can get the whole banknote out without toppling the bottle.

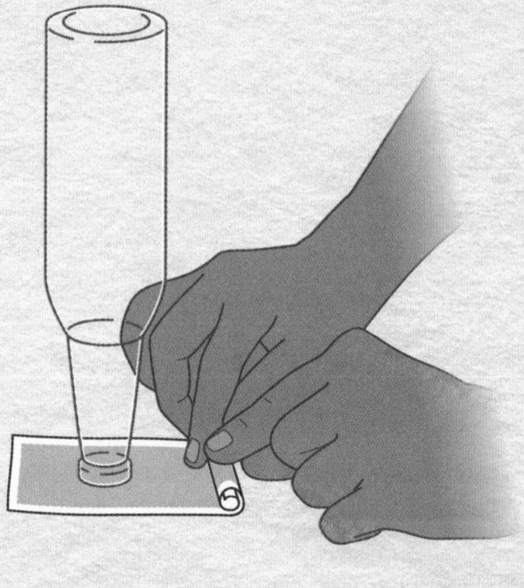

Roll the note gently and smoothly, keeping a constant pressure on the bottle once you reach it.

207. COUNT THE TIME

With a 7-minute hourglass and an 11-minute hourglass, what is the simplest way to time exactly **15 MINUTES?**

Solution on page 222

208. WATER CARRIER

I have holes in my top and bottom, my left and right and in the middle. But I still hold water.

WHAT AM I?

Solution on page 222

209. ART GALLERY

4+ players
Use your imagination and creativity to turn yourself into an expert gallery guide.

WHAT YOU WILL NEED:

- Pencils and paper for everyone
- A stopwatch

WHAT YOU MUST DO:

This game involves a whole range of skills, fun and playacting, but you don't have to be an expert in any area to join in and have lots of laughs.

There are no winners or losers in this game – the emphasis is on having fun. Everyone is given a sheet of paper and a pencil. You must then draw the silliest thing you can. Anything that comes into your head will do – a weird shape, a strange face, a building or simply an abstract pattern.

After ten minutes or so, everyone puts their drawings in the middle of the table and each player has to pick one at random. The players then have two minutes to study the drawing.

Everyone then takes it in turns to act like an art gallery guide and describe exactly what is in the drawing, invent some history behind the artwork or explain what was going through the artist's mind when he or she created it.

The sillier the drawings are, the more entertaining the gallery guides' explanations will be!

210. LESS BUT MORE?

What number less than 100 increases by one-fifth of its value when its digits are reversed?

Solution on page 222

211. DAY-TO-DAY

The day after tomorrow is the third day after Wednesday.

WHAT WAS THE DAY BEFORE YESTERDAY?

Solution on page 222

212. THE FORTUNE TELLER

2+ players
Use this paper gadget to predict people's fortunes.

WHAT YOU WILL NEED:

- A square sheet of paper about 216 mm (8.5 inches) square
- A pencil

WHAT YOU MUST DO:

First you must make your basic FortuneTeller. Fold the paper in half diagonally to create a triangle. Unfold and then fold it in half again in the opposite direction. Your square should now have fold marks dividing it into four triangles.

Fold one corner into the centre spot and crease the fold by rubbing your thumbnail along it to hold it in place. Fold the other three corners into the centre as well.

Now turn the paper over and fold each corner of your new square into the centre. You should be left with eight triangles facing you. Using the pencil, number these triangles from 1 to 8. Then lift up the flaps and beneath each number write a different 'fortune' – a short phrase such as 'You will find great riches in foreign lands' or 'You will become a great leader'.

Once you have written eight 'fortunes', close all the flaps and fold your FortuneTeller in half. You will now have four pockets on the outside, two facing you and two behind. Slip your thumbs and forefingers into the pocket and push them out to form a tent-like structure.

You should now be able to push your fingers apart forwards to open the 'mouth' of the FortuneTeller, pull them back to the middle to close it and then pull them out to the sides to open it in the other direction. You will be able to see different numbers inside when you open it forwards from those you see when you open it sideways.

Once you have the FortuneTeller working, you can flatten it and draw pictures of animals on the outside of the finger pockets. The animals will be the first choice that you give when you are telling someone's fortune. If you have, for example, drawn an elephant, a penguin, a giraffe and a monkey, you must ask your subject to choose which of the animals they like best. If the elephant is chosen, you then work your FortuneTeller open and closed, calling out one letter for each move: E-L-E-P-H-A-N-T.

You then hold the FortuneTeller open on the final move and ask your subject to choose a number from those in view. If 4 is in view and is chosen, you work the FortuneTeller open and closed four times and ask your subject to choose another number.

This is where the subject's fortune is actually told because now you flatten the Fortune Teller on the table, opening it up with all of the numbers showing. You lift the flap marked with the chosen number and read what is written under the flap.

1.

2.

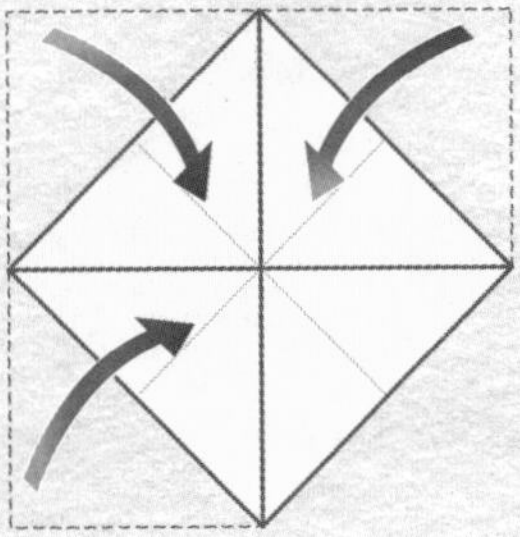

3.

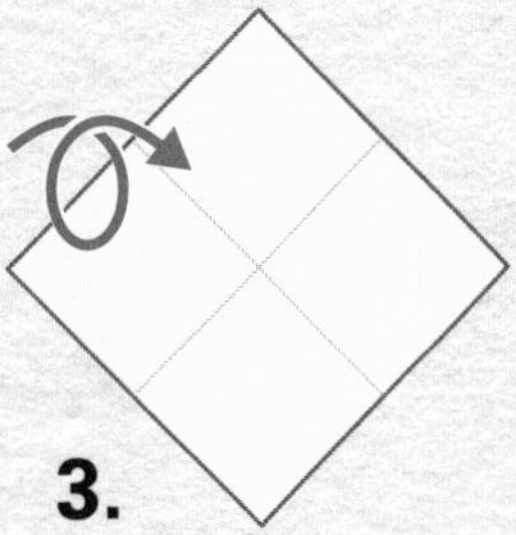

4.

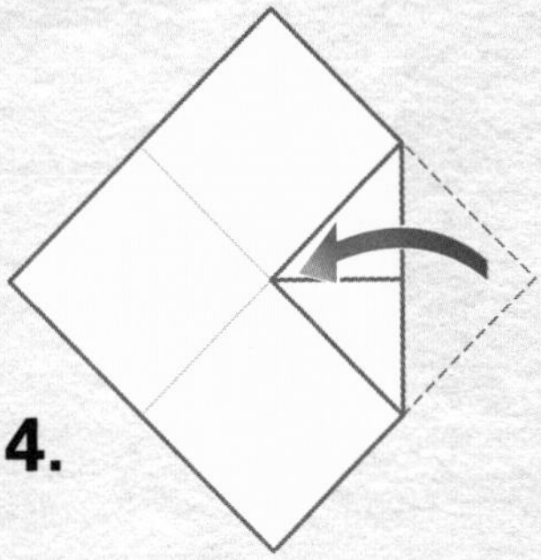

5.

6.

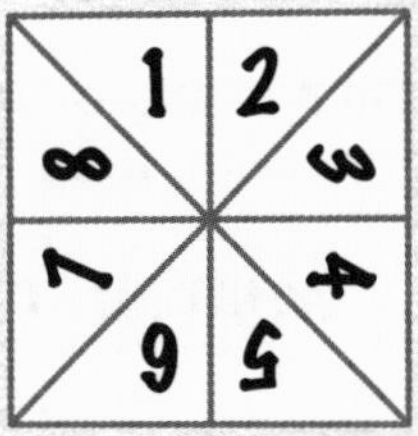

7.

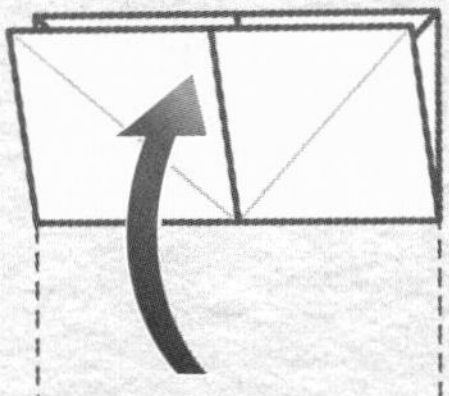

1. Fold one corner into the middle.
2. Repeat with the other corners.
3. Turn the paper over.
4. Fold one corner into the middle.
5. Repeat with the other corners.
6. Mark with numbers 1 to 8
7. Fold in half, then open out by pushing your fingers inside.
8. Flatten to draw pictures round the outside.

8.

TIP
Create a new FortuneTeller with different fortunes once all of the old fortunes have been told.

213. HORSE INCIDENT

A horse jumped over a tower and landed on a man, the man disappeared.

WHAT JUST HAPPENED?

Solution on page 222

214. CONUNDRUM

I have an end but no beginning, a home but no family, a space but no room. I can give any name and there is no word I can't produce, yet I never speak.

WHAT AM I?

Solution on page 222

215. TEAM SPIRIT

At a nature reserve, the volunteer guides are to be organised into two teams for training, The Bear Team and The Eagle Team. Each guide has to have either an eagle or a bear badge pinned to his or her hat. All of the guides have been allocated to a team except three – Jane, Freddy and Mike. There are five badges left – three eagles and two bears. For fun, Jane, Freddy and Mike are blindfolded and the others pin a badge onto their hats. The remaining two badges are then hidden and Jane, Freddy and Mike are allowed to remove their blindfolds.

The three have been positioned so that Jane can see Freddy and Mike's badges, Mike can see Freddy's badge and Freddy can't see anyone's badge.

When they are asked whether they have eagle or bear badges, Jane says that she doesn't know and Mike also says that he doesn't know.

Freddy says, 'I'm in The Eagle Team!'

HOW DID HE KNOW?

Solution on page 222

216. ACROSTICS

2+ players
Guess the word by working out the clues.

WHAT YOU WILL NEED:

- Pencil and paper for each player

WHAT YOU MUST DO:

Decide on a topic. Each person must then think of a word concerned with that topic. If the topic is buildings, the word might be 'office' or 'palace'.

Write down your word, but keep it to yourself. Then think of clues for other words that start with each of the letters of your chosen word.

Palace might work like this:

He catches criminals	Policeman
It's not before, it's	After
A giggle that exploded	Laugh
Small crawling insect	Ant
A vehicle with wheels	Car
It contains only one letter	Envelope

Each player takes it in turn to give a clue and the others must write down the letter to which they think the clue points.

When it is your turn to give a clue, you can also try to guess one other player's word. You get a point for each one you guess correctly and the player with the most points at the end of your acrostic session is the winner.

217. NUMBER MAGIC

2+ players
Find a number someone has thought of and then tell them their age.

WHAT YOU WILL NEED:

- Pencils and paper for everyone and a calculator if required

WHAT YOU MUST DO:

Ask everyone to think of a five-digit number. Then double it.
Then add 5. Then multiply it by 50. Then add their age.
Then add the number of days in the year (365). Finally, subtract 615.

The answer will be a seven-figure number. The first five numbers will be the number first thought of, and the last two will be the player's age.

Let's say you thought of the number	21,485
Double it	42,970
Add 5	42,975
Multiply by 50	2,148,750
Add your age (we'll say you're 12)	2,148,762
Add 365	2,149,127
Subtract 615	2,148,512

Ask each player to show you their answers and you will be able to tell them the number they first thought of and their age – providing they did their sums correctly!

218. GET DIGGING

If it takes one man three days to dig a hole, how long would it take two men to dig **HALF A HOLE?**

Solution on page 222

219. RIDDLE

A stick I found that weighed two pounds:
I sawed it up one day.
In pieces eight of equal weight,
how much did each piece weigh?

Solution on page 222

220. HEADS AND FEET

A farmer has chickens roaming around a field where cows are grazing. He tries to count them. He counts 8 heads and 28 feet.

HOW MANY COWS DOES HE HAVE AND HOW MANY CHICKENS

Solution on page 223

221. FATHERS AND SONS

A man joins a small group looking at a portrait. He studies the portrait for a moment and then says, "Brothers and sisters I have none, but that man's father is my father's son."

WHO IS IN THE PORTRAIT?

Solution on page 223

222. ANAGRAMS

2+ players
Sort out the jumbled letters quickest to win the points.

WHAT YOU WILL NEED:

- Lots of sheets of paper
- Pencils for everyone

WHAT YOU MUST DO:

One player must act as the judge, and everyone takes a turn at being the judge.

Each player is given a piece of paper and a pencil. The judge calls out a topic. It might be 'Animals' or 'Cities'. Everyone must then write down the name of an animal or a city, using big letters but taking care that no one else sees.

They then work out an anagram of that name – a word or phrase that uses the same letters. 'Horse' could become 'shore' or 'Rome' could become 'more'. Keep your working out on the same side of the paper, then turn the paper over to write your new word or phrase on the back.

Each person in turn holds up their anagram for everyone to see and the first person to call out the original word gets a point. The judge can join in calling out the solutions, but does not write down an anagram.

The person sitting to the right of the judge now takes on the judge's role and must think of a new topic.

223. HEAVY BURDEN

Carrying my burden would break a rich man's back. I have no riches but can leave silver in my track.

WHAT AM I?

Solution on page 223

224. LETTER SEQUENCE

What comes next in this sequence?

O T T F F S S ? ? ?

Solution on page 223

HINT
Are these just random letters, or does each letter perhaps stand for something?

225. THE SECRET COIN

2+ players
Make a coin vanish from the palm of your hand.

WHAT YOU WILL NEED:

- Four coins
- Some silver foil the same shade as the coins
- Scissors

WHAT YOU MUST DO:

Preparation and practice, as always with conjuring tricks, are essential to make it look like a coin in your hand has simply vanished.

The preparation involves making a fake coin. Cover one side and the edges of one of the coins with the silver foil (you can use other colours of foil for different types of coin) and press the foil against the coin, rubbing it with your thumb.

The foil will take on an impression of the coin. You must then carefully remove it from the coin so that it retains its shape. Trim off any excess foil, but make sure to leave the foil that was round the rim of the coin so that your fake coin will look like it is as thick as a normal coin.

With your fake coin prepared, you are ready to go in front of your audience. Show the audience four coins in your hand. It's best if the three real ones can conceal the fake coin a little.

You can then clap your hands closed, rub them together and make a big show of telling your audience that simply by rubbing your hands together you can make one of the coins vanish.

What you will actually be doing is scrunching up your fake coin. With a little practice, you should be able to roll it into a ball small enough to hide between your fingers when you open your hands again.

As far as your audience is concerned, one of the coins will simply have disappeared.

1.

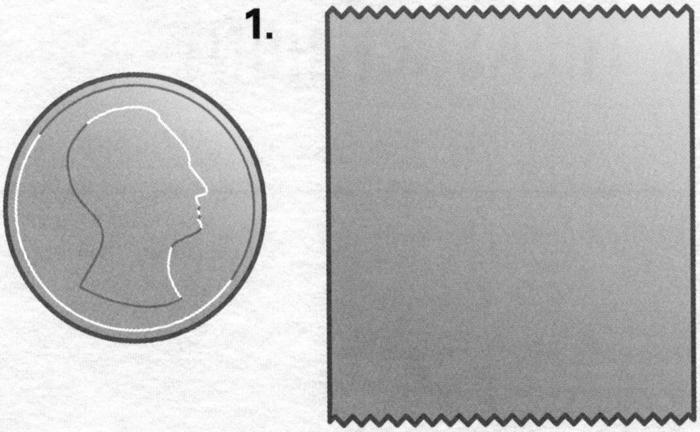

1. The foil that you use should be a little bigger than the coin and roughly the same shade.

2.

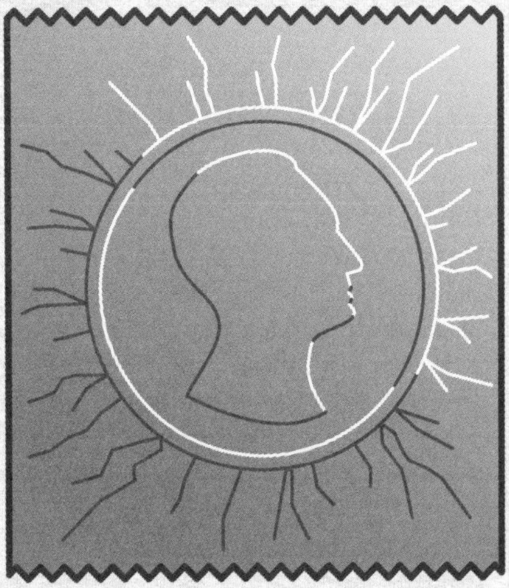

2. Gently rub the foil until it takes on the impression of the coin, then fold the foil down around the edges to give your fake coin some depth.

3.

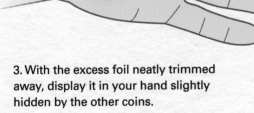

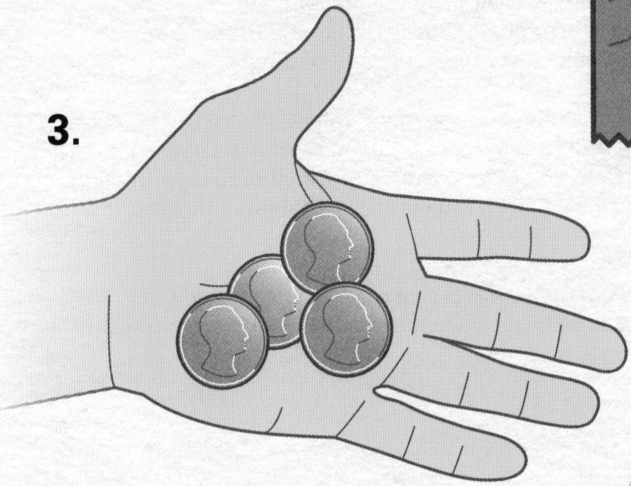

3. With the excess foil neatly trimmed away, display it in your hand slightly hidden by the other coins.

TIP

You need to be able to hide the scrunched-up fake coin effectively, and to do that you will have to put in a bit of practice before you try this trick out on an audience.

226. TREASURE HUNT

4+ players
Find the clues that lead to the treasure horde.

WHAT YOU WILL NEED:

- Ten pieces of paper
- A pencil
- A big bag of wrapped sweets

WHAT YOU MUST DO:

This is an ideal game for parents or older kids to set up for younger children and requires a little preparation. The first thing to do is to choose a hiding place for your treasure horde of sweets.

Next, write out ten clues and hide them around the house, in the garden or anywhere to which the treasure hunters will have easy access. If there are lots of treasure hunters, split them into teams but make it clear from the outset that there is a treasure chest – a bowl or a large plate sitting on a table, to which all of the treasure must be brought to be divided up fairly between everyone at the end of the game.

Now you give or read out a clue and send your treasure hunters off to try to work it out. The clue could be something like, 'I am a city in England that keeps you clean.' They will quickly work out that is Bath and rush to the bathroom where they will find the next clue in the bath, along with a couple of sweets to keep them interested in the treasure.

The clues eventually lead to the big bag of sweets that can then be shared out. You can do more than ten clues but the more clues there are, the longer the treasure hunt will take.

TIP
Try to keep the clues light-hearted and be on hand to give hints to younger children if they are struggling to work them out.

227. MAGIC BALL

A magician claims to be able to throw a ball so that it goes a short distance, stops, turns round and comes back again, without him bouncing it off any object or tying anything to the ball.

HOW DOES HE DO IT?

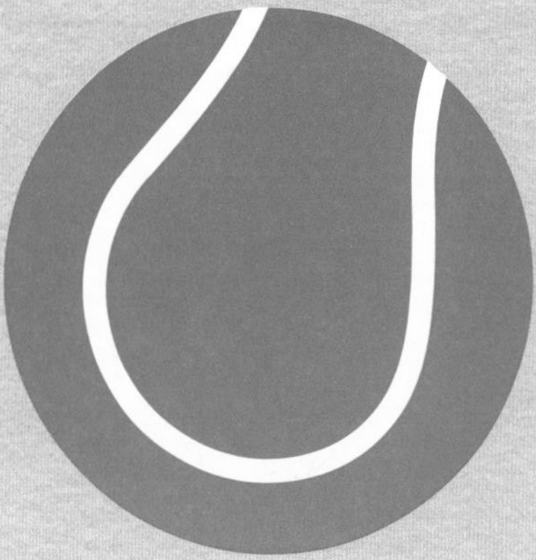

Solution on page 223

228. NOT SO HANDY

I have hands but they cannot grip.
My hands can point but they cannot clap.

WHAT AM I?

Solution on page 223

229. STRANGE SPEARS

Shining downward-thrusting spears
that shed no rust but sometimes tears.

WHAT ARE THEY?

Solution on page 223

230. COLOURFUL HOUSES

Three bungalows stood in a row – one blue, one pink and one green. Absolutely everything in the blue house, including the carpets, curtains, furniture and walls, was blue. Similarly, everything in the pink house was pink and everything in the green house was green.

WHAT COLOUR WERE THE STAIRS IN THE BLUE HOUSE?

Solution on page 223

231. WORD BUILDER

2+ players
You can improve your spelling and vocabulary with this game, but the aim is never to finish writing a word.

WHAT YOU WILL NEED:

- Paper and pencil
- A dictionary

WHAT YOU MUST DO:

The first player writes a letter on the piece of paper. The next player adds a letter that could go towards building a word and each player in turn adds a letter, always making sure that the letter they add could be the next part of a word. If challenged, they have to say the word that they think could be made. Ultimately, one player will have to add a letter that completes the word and that player loses a 'life'. Lose six lives and you are out of the game.

For example, if four players were playing:

Player 1 writes	P	
Player 2 writes	R	This could make 'prove' or 'pram', etc
Player 3 writes	A	'Pram' is still a possibility, or 'prairie'
Player 4 writes	C	Now we could have 'practice'
Player 1 writes	T	'Practice' looks like it might end up as the word
Player 2 writes	I	'Practice' is still on
Player 3 writes	C	'Practice' would mean Player 4 loses a life
Player 4 writes	A	Player 4 has saved a life by aiming for 'practical'
Player 1 writes	L	Player 1 loses a life

Player 1 could have written B instead of L, aiming for 'practicable', but would have to have known that word.

Three-letter words make the game too short. Words like 'the' or 'and' can be expanded to make 'theory' or 'android', so never end on a three-letter word, but do keep a dictionary handy to settle any disputes!

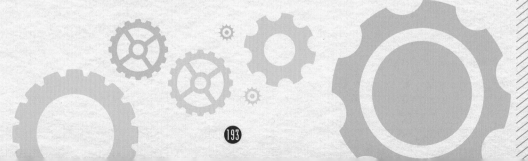

232. TRICKY TRIANGLE

How many triangles are in the image?

Solution on page 223

233. SHADY CIRCLES

Shade in the white circles in such a way that the numbers in the boxes indicate how many dark circles surround them.

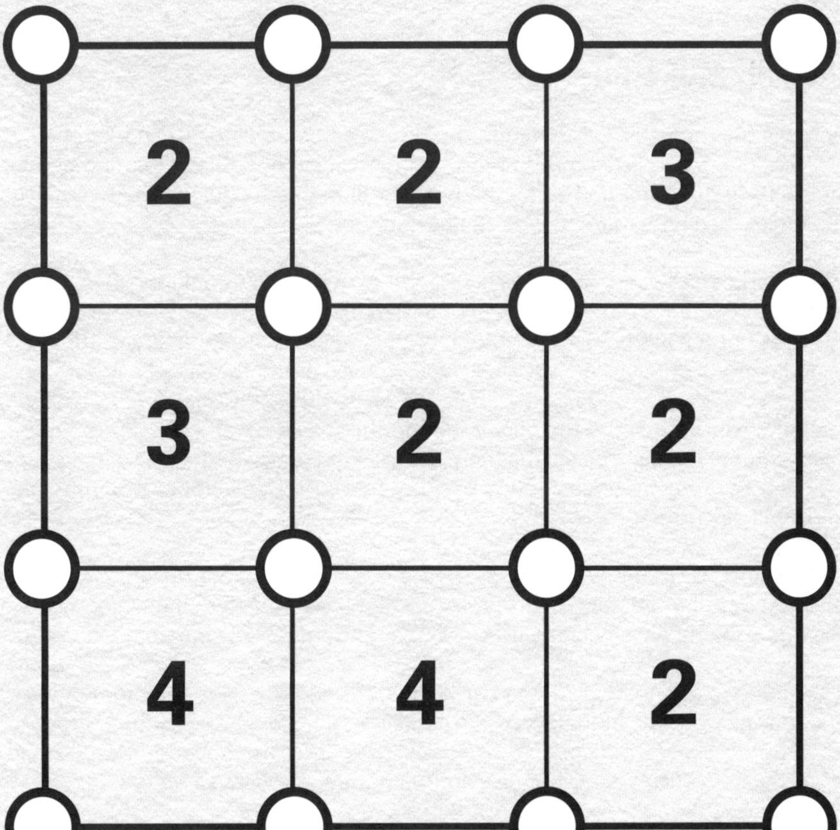

Solution on page 223

234. IT'S IN THE CARDS

2+ players
Read the mind of your willing volunteer to find the mystery card.

WHAT YOU WILL NEED:

- A pack of cards that you don't mind marking

WHAT YOU MUST DO:

Prepare this trick secretly beforehand. Shuffle the cards and split the pack in half. On the backs of one half, write random numbers between 1 and 52 but with no eights. On the backs of the other half, write the number 8 on every one. Put the two halves together with the cards marked 8 on the bottom.

Show a volunteer a fan spread of the cards. Be sure to fan out only those cards from the bottom of the deck, the ones that are all marked 8 on the back. Do not let anyone see the backs of the cards. Ask the volunteer to choose a card mentally, without touching it, and to concentrate on it because you are going to read his or her mind.

Close up the cards, covering the deck with your hands so no one can see the number. Look like you are concentrating, then say, 'Your card was an eight.' That's unlikely to be true, but if it is, then you have already performed a trick – well done! It is more likely that they will say no.

Deal a few cards from the top of the deck face down to show that they have numbers on the back. Say, 'I am getting a strong sense that it was an eight. I have numbered these cards so that I always know they are in a random order. None of these is yours.'

Look like you are giving up. Turn the cards in your hand over and fan them out. Ask the volunteer to pick out the hidden card. As it has come from what was the bottom half of the deck, you can take the card, turn it over and say, 'Ah, this is what was confusing me ...' because on the back is written the number 8.

TIP

Don't let anyone see that ALL of the cards from that part of the deck have 8 on the back. Put the cards away before they can be examined.

235. RHYME TIME

2+ players
A guessing game where you find the missing word through rhyme.

WHAT YOU WILL NEED:

- Paper and pencils for each player

WHAT YOU MUST DO:

Decide who is to go first. That player must then think of a word, write it down but not let anyone see it.

The player then gives a clue by saying, 'I know a word that rhymes with ...' and give a rhyming word. If the mystery word that the player wrote down was, for example, 'head', the player could say, 'I know a word that rhymes with red.'

Each player then takes it in turns to ask a question, without mentioning the word they think might be the mystery word.

A player might ask, 'Is it somewhere you might sleep?' The first player would then say, 'No, it's not bed'.

Play then continues until someone asks a question to which the answer is yes, such as, 'Is it a part of your body?' The first player will answer 'yes' and the questioner can then say 'Is it head?' The first player must then show the word on the paper to confirm that the guess is correct.

The player who guesses correctly then starts the game again by writing down a new word and giving a new rhyming clue.

236. IN A DAZE

A teacher asked a pupil if he could name three days of the week that come one after the other, but without using Tuesday, Friday or Sunday.

WHAT DID HE SAY?

Solution on page 224

237. NO ESCAPE

An explorer out trekking alone comes across a bear and stops, standing dead still. The bear doesn't spot him and the explorer decides to make a run for it before the bear realizes that he is there.

In order to confuse the bear, should it follow his tracks, he runs a mile south, then a mile west, then a mile north. To his dismay, he finds the bear waiting for him, although the bear has not moved at all.

WHAT COLOUR IS THE BEAR?

Solution on page 224

238. FIFTEENS

2+ players
This game takes more concentration and strategy than it might seem.

WHAT YOU WILL NEED:

- Fifteen toothpicks

WHAT YOU MUST DO:

This simple game is said to have originated in ancient China and is a more advanced form of Pick Up Sticks (see page 45). It involves fifteen toothpicks (or you can use coins or playing cards) arranged in a particular way.

The toothpicks are in seven rows. There is one in the first row. Beneath that there are two in the second row. Beneath that there are three in the third row, then two more rows of three, a row of two and a final single toothpick.

You and your opponent must take it in turns to pick up toothpicks. You can pick up one from a row, or two, or the complete row, but you can only take from one row at a time.

The last one to pick up a toothpick is the winner.

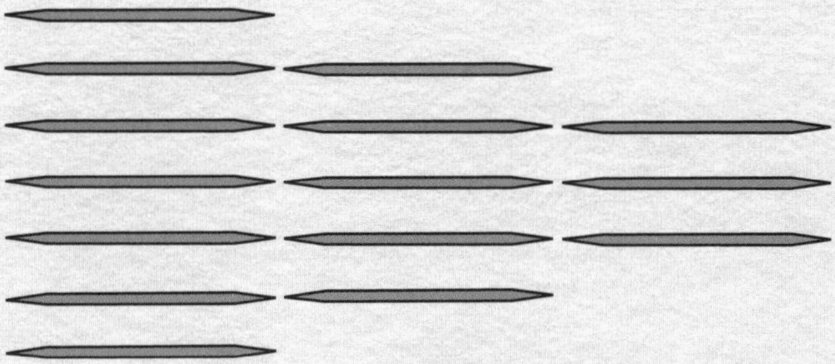

239. CHEAT

4+ players
In this card game the biggest cheat is usually the winner.

WHAT YOU WILL NEED:

- A pack of cards (two packs if there are more than four players)

WHAT YOU MUST DO:

The dealer deals out all of the cards. The players look at their cards and the player to the dealer's left goes first. He or she places up to four cards face down in the middle of the table to start a discard pile. Players have to announce what they are placing down and their discards must be sets. They can have a 'run' of four of the same suit – the four, five, six and seven of spades, for example. They can also have four of a kind – four threes, four nines or four kings, perhaps.

No one sees what is being discarded, but if a player says they are discarding four fives and you have three fives in your hand, they are obviously cheating (although it's not so easy to tell when you are playing with two packs) and you yell 'Cheat!'

The last cards to be discarded are then turned over. If the player who played them was cheating, that player has to take all of the cards from the discard pile. If the player who called 'Cheat!' was wrong, that player has to take all of the cards.

The first person to get rid of all of their cards is the winner.

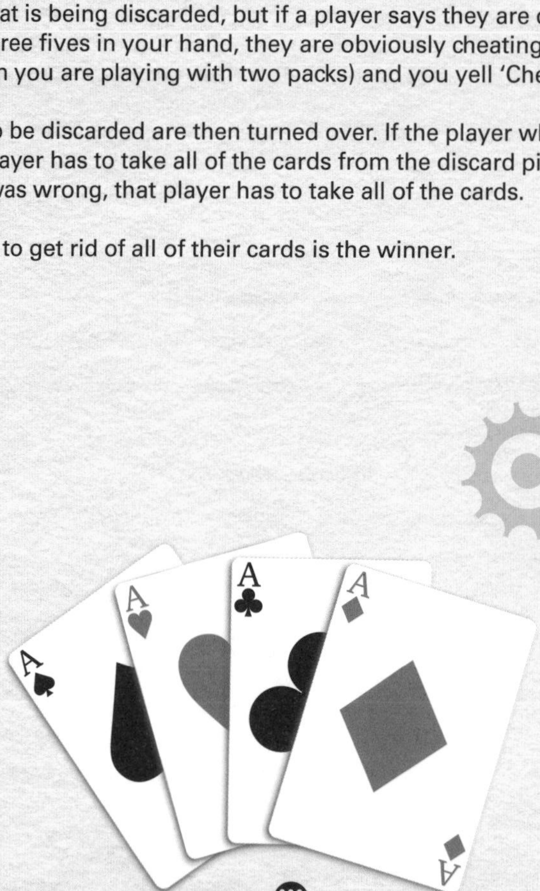

240. MISSING SYMBOLS

8 8 8 8 8 8 8 8 = 1,000.

Using only addition symbols (+) between the eights, make this sum work.

HINT
It will probably take a bit of trial and error to get the solution to this problem.

Solution on page 224

241. HALF GIRLS

A man has seven children. Half of them are daughters.

HOW CAN THIS BE?

Solution on page 224

242. STANDING ROLL

2+ players
This trick looks impossible, even when you see it working before your very eyes!

WHAT YOU WILL NEED:

- A cardboard tube from inside a toilet roll

WHAT YOU MUST DO:

Challenge your friends to drop the tube onto a table so that it stands up, vertically, balanced on one end.

Most people will drop the tube so that it hits the table end first, thinking that that is the best way to finish with a standing cardboard column, but the tube will bounce and fall over.

The way to make it stand on end is actually to drop it so that it lands on its side. It will then bounce up and stand on one end. You will have to practise a bit to find the right height from which to drop it. Somewhere around 15 cm (6 inches) tends to work.

It may not bounce and stand up every time, but you can expect it to work at least once in every three drops.

TIP
If this trick doesn't work for you first time, keep trying but also try dropping the toilet roll with a little force to make sure that it bounces.

243. PIN THE TAIL ON THE DONKEY

2+ players
Nothing seems easier than finding the donkey's rear end to restore its tail, but you'll be amazed where that poor donkey's tail ends up!

WHAT YOU WILL NEED:

• A blindfold • A large sheet of paper that can be hung on a wall (a leftover length of wallpaper is ideal) • A strip of paper to represent the donkey's tail • A marker pen • A ruler

WHAT YOU MUST DO:

Mark the basic outline of a donkey on the paper, making it as big as possible, but don't give it a tail. Mark with an X roughly where the tail should be so it can be measured against later.

Each player then takes a turn at being blindfolded and attempting to place the donkey's tail in the right position. They start from the same point right in front of the donkey, three or four steps back from the wall. Before they set off they gently turn round three times. Make sure there are others on each side to stop the player wandering off in totally the wrong direction.

The player then has to hold the tail against the illustration where he or she thinks it should go. Actually pinning the tail to the wall is not necessary. The blindfold is removed and a mark made on the illustration with the player's initials beside it.

Closest to the pre-marked tail site – the ruler can be used to decide – is the winner.

244. UNFILLABLE

What is no bigger than a saucepan, can be held in your hand like a saucepan but no amount of water can fill it up?

Solution on page 224

245. SUM TOTAL

Complete the sum using the numbers 0–9 once (three has already been used):

3 X - - - - (4 DIGITS) = - - - - - (5 DIGITS)

Solution on page 224

246. NUMBER JUMBLER

Using only digits 1 to 9, just once each, how can you make three numbers, each of three digits, where the second number is twice the first number and the third number is three times the first number?

Solution on page 224

247. LUCKY WINNERS

Two fathers and two sons win a fortune on the lottery and go out together to buy new cars. They buy three brand-new luxury cars – one car each.

HOW CAN THIS BE?

Solution on page 224

248. CONSEQUENCES

2+ players
Take it in turns to write a line of a story that will have a surprise ending.

WHAT YOU WILL NEED:

- A sheet of paper for each player
- A pencil for each player

WHAT YOU MUST DO:

Each player writes an adjective at the top of his or her sheet, describing a man. It could say 'Happy' or you can write more, such as 'Very angry, wearing pink socks'.

The first line is folded over and the sheet passed to the left so that everyone has a different sheet to add the next line at the top of the page. The next line must be a man's name. It can be someone you all know, or a completely made-up name. The paper is then folded over and passed on once more for the next new line to be added.

The sequence of lines goes as follows:

1. Adjective or phrase describing a man
2. A man's name
3. The word MET followed by an adjective or phrase describing a woman
4. A woman's name
5. The word AT followed by the place where they met
6. The words HE SAID followed by what he said
7. The words SHE SAID followed by what she said
8. The words THE CONSEQUENCE WAS followed by what happened
9. The words THE WORLD THOUGHT followed by what everyone thought about it

Once everyone has written what the world thought about the meeting, pass the papers on one more time, open them up and take turns to read out the ridiculous stories!

249. MEET AND GREET

A mother and her daughter are walking down the street when they meet a man and both say, 'Hello, Father'.

HOW CAN THIS BE?

Solution on page 224

250. HARD WORKER

I am used from head to toe and the harder I work, the smaller I grow.

WHAT AM I?

Solution on page 224

HINT
This hard worker may grow smaller but comes in all different shapes and sizes.

251. SNAKE TRAP

2+ players
The snake has poisonous fangs and mustn't be allowed to bite itself!

WHAT YOU WILL NEED:

- Pencil and paper

WHAT YOU MUST DO:

Mark a grid of dots on the paper, ten dots wide by ten dots deep. The dots should be about 1.25 cm (half an inch) apart. The first player then draws a line connecting two dots. The line can be vertical or horizontal but not diagonal. The second player adds another line connecting one end of the first line to an adjacent dot. The line can go across, or up, or down, but not diagonally.

You can add lines to either end of the snake and it can go anywhere on the grid, but neither end of the snake is allowed to touch its body. This, you see, is a highly poisonous snake with a head at either end and if it bites itself, it dies.

The players must try to draw their lines in such a way that they force their opponent to be the one who must eventually draw the line that turns the snake on itself.

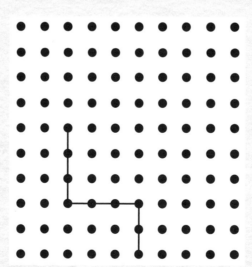

252. BLOW FOOTBALL

2+ players
The player or team with the most puff wins!

WHAT YOU WILL NEED:

- A drinking straw for each player
- A ping-pong ball (or scrunched-up paper ball)
- Books, mugs or other items to act as goalposts

WHAT YOU MUST DO:

Set up your goals at either end of a table, or on the floor. Each player then chooses a position around the table or around the floorspace chosen as a 'pitch'. Players must not move from their positions, although they can lean and stretch as much as they like. The ball is placed in the centre of the table, and the game begins when someone shouts 'Blow!' The two players closest to the ball must then blow through their straws to send the ball towards the opposition goal.

As the ball comes within range, other players join in to blow the ball away from their goal or towards the other goal.

The winners are the players who have scored most goals by the time everyone has run out of breath!

PUZZLES AND RIDDLES ANSWERS

01. A key.

02. Twice. Load it once with two selections of three balls, leaving three aside. If one of the selections is heavier, the heavy ball is one of those three. If both selections weigh exactly the same, the heavy ball is one of the three set aside. You have now established which of the sets of three contains the heavy ball. Load the scales a second time, placing one of the suspect balls on each side and leaving one out. If one of the balls on the scales is heavier, it will be obvious and if they both weigh the same, then the heavy ball is the one you left out.

04. Put five in the first cup, five in the second cup and then put the second cup in the third cup.

05. They were playing different opponents.

06. Harry knows that the 'apples and pears' label is wrong, so he picks one fruit from there. He then knows whether that box contains apples or pears and can put the correct label on it. If it was an apple, for example, he can then transfer the 'pears' label to the box that was marked 'apples' and put the 'apples and pears' label on the one that was marked 'pears'.

07. Kevin, Brian, Simon, Alan, Ian.

10. Take the second glass, pour it into the fifth glass and put it back.

11. Seven – there is only one brother but he is brother to all of the girls.

12. Heartbeats.

14. It wasn't raining.

15. 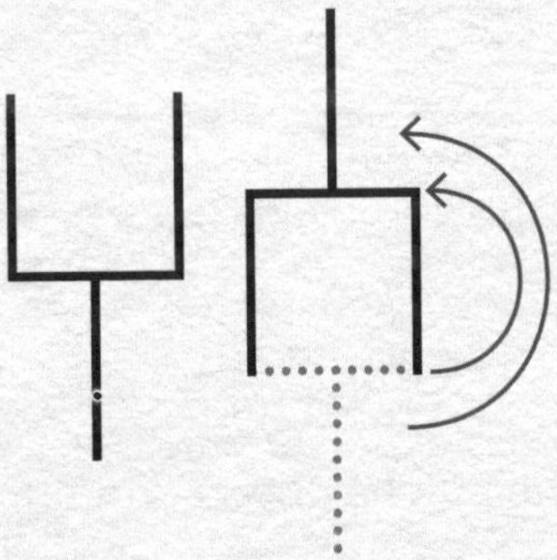

18. The girl has 7 and the boy has 5.

19. Mount Everest. It was still there, even though it hadn't been discovered.

20. Jump off the bottom rung.

21. Three to be sure, two if you're lucky.

23. Two hours. James will eat 54 (27 per hour), Sarah will eat 24 (12 per hour) and Dominic will eat 42 (21 per hour).

24. Your tongue.

27. 40

28. One. After that it is no longer an <u>empty</u> garage.

30. 301. If it chews through the first page of Vol 1, then (not counting covers) it is straight on to the last page of Vol 2. It goes all the way through Vol 2 and stops at the last page of Vol 3, which is next to the first page of Vol 2.

34. Sawdust.

35. Blame.

36. They are two of triplets.

37. She gives ten children an apple and the 11th child the bowl with the apple in it.

38. Footsteps.

39. None. All of the soil has been dug out of the hole.

42.

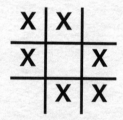

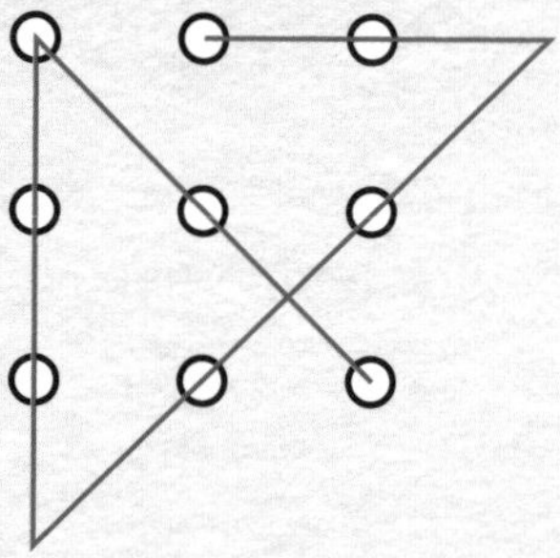

43. Name.

44.

X	X	
X		X
	X	X

45. The answer is actually deceptively simple for anyone who has studied the radius and circumference of circles at school. The circumference of a circle is 2 x pi x radius. We take the value of pi to be 3.14. Because we are looking for the extra length of string we will need, we are calculating the difference between the first circumference (the string laid along the ground) and the second (the string held one metre [3.3 feet] from the ground). The difference between the first radius and the second is one metre, so the difference between the circumferences is: 2 x 3.14 x 1m = 6.28m

47.

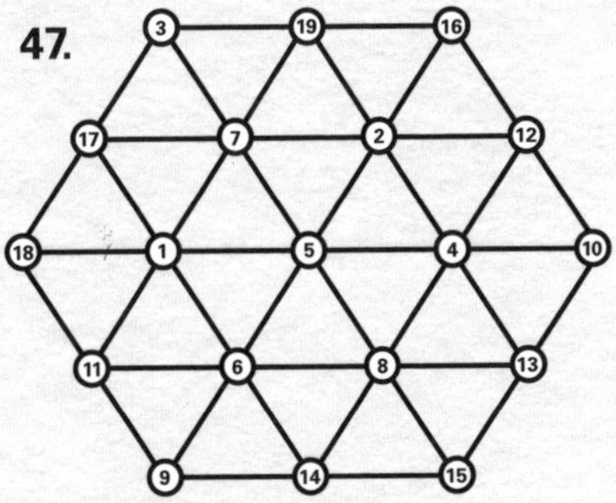

49.

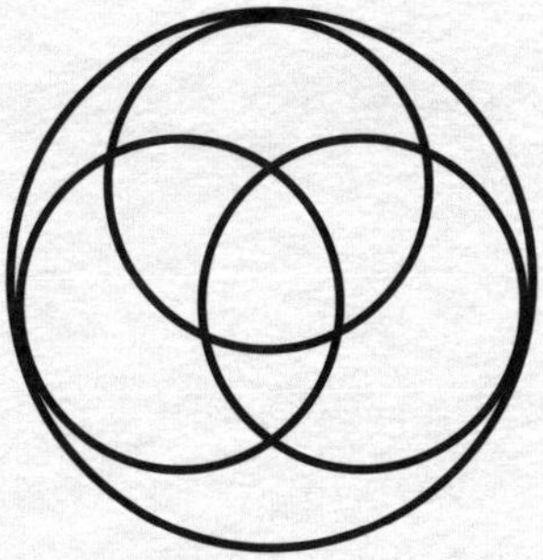

51. The parrot is deaf.

52. David.

53. 99 + (9÷9) = 100

57. A mirror.

58.

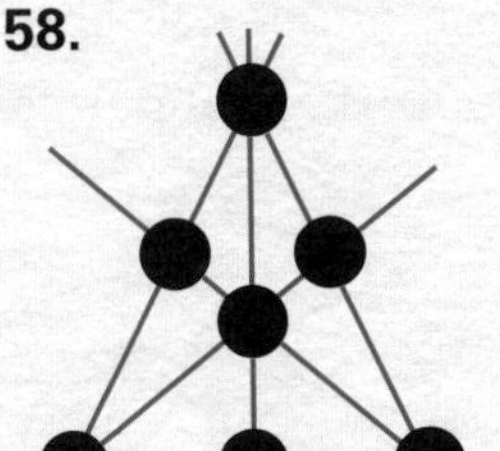

59.

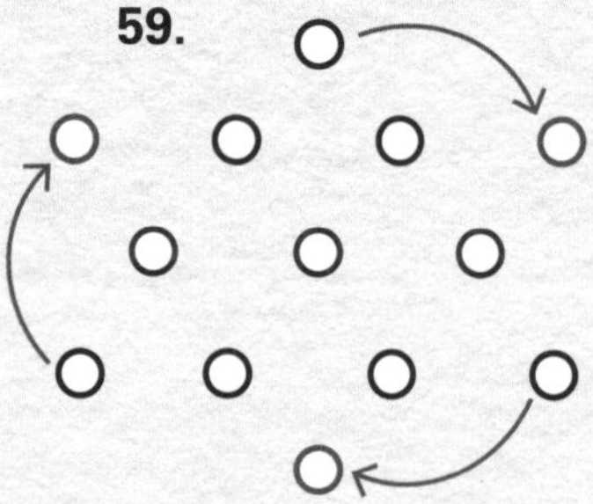

61. Silence.

62. Most creatures. Buildings can't jump.

63. Stars.

64. None. The bigger ones would be willing to shake hands when they met a giant smaller than themselves, but the smaller ones would refuse.

66.

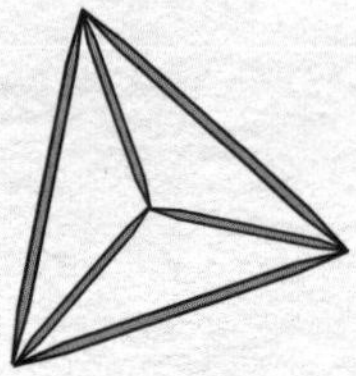

68. Skeleton Pete puts one gold doubloon into one chest and everything else in the other. Once he is blindfolded, if he chooses the chest with the single gold doubloon, he has won and if he chooses the other chest, he still has almost a 50 per cent chance of winning.

71.

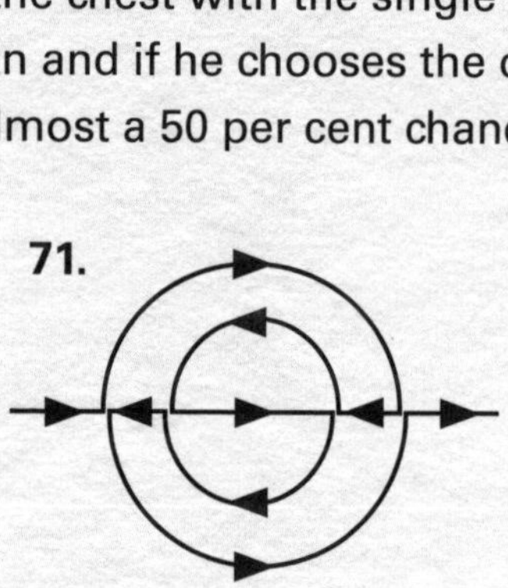

74. I am a girl – a daughter, not a son.

75. Darkness.

78. His old university friend was a woman called Sarah.

79. Nothing.

80. 312211 (three ones, two twos, one one)

81 Second.

82. Someone's temper.

84. His horse was called Friday.

85. Yesterday.

86.

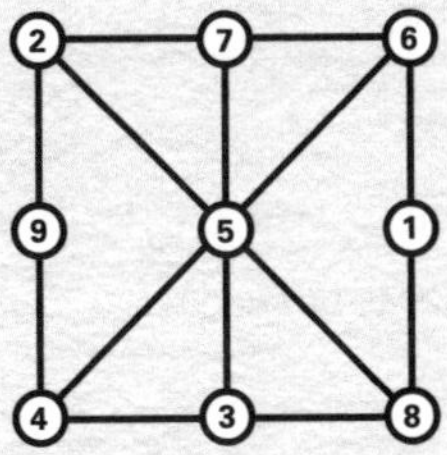

87. The stair carpet.

88. It is her 15th birthday.

91. Cut it in half in the normal way, then make another cut all the way across to cut it into quarters, then slice the cake in half horizontally.

92. An egg.

94. He's still alive – 'living in England.'

95. A secret.

96. The one with the biggest head.

97. The bus driver is walking.

99. Billy. Today must be Thursday.

100. A sponge.

101. An umbrella.

102. On a map.

103. 16th day.

104. The telephone.

107. O N D – they are the months of the year (October, November, December).

108. It is daytime.

109. It takes three turns. Turn three up. Turn two up and one down. Turn three up.

112.

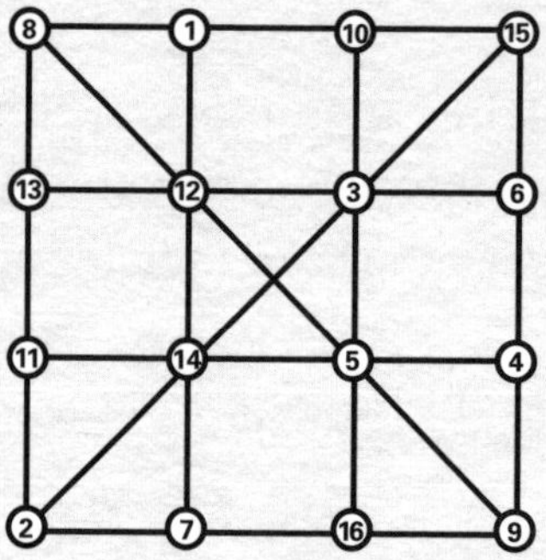

This is just one of many possible solutions.

117. You could be incredibly lucky and pick out three matching pairs straight away by choosing just six socks, but if you rule out chance altogether, you will have to pick out the 2 red socks, 4 yellow socks and 5 of each of the other colours. You have now hauled 46 socks out of the drawer and need just one more to be sure of having 6 matching socks (three pairs), so the answer is 47.

118. Three, one in New York, one in Paris and one in London.

119. Tilt the glass at an angle until the water is right at the lip of the glass, about to pour out. At this point, if it is touching the top edge at the bottom of the glass, then the glass is half full. If the water is only part way up the bottom of the glass, it is less than half full. If it is part way up the top edge of the glass, it is more than half full.

121. L8 – upside down these are the numbers from 86 to 91.

122. Thursday.

125. Are you asleep?

126. The door to the room.

127. There are at least seven family members.

128. This is one of the oldest and most famous riddles of all time. The Sphinx is said to have guarded the entrance to the Greek city of Thebes, and to have asked this riddle to travellers. Those who could not answer were eaten. The Greek hero, Oedipus, solved the riddle by answering: Man – who crawls on all fours as a baby, then walks on two feet as an adult, then uses a walking stick in old age.

131. He fills the 3-gallon jug and pours it into the 5-gallon jug. He then has 2 gallons of space left in the 5-gallon jug. He fills the 3-gallon jug again and uses it to fill up the 5-gallon jug. Two gallons are used, leaving 1 gallon in the 3-gallon jug.

134.

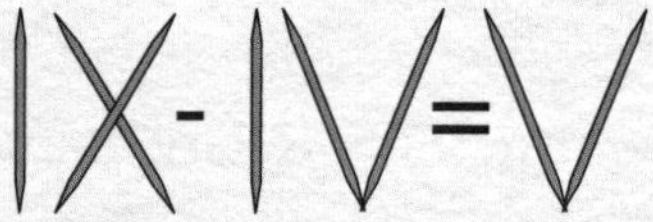

135. He is ten.

136. They are in different time zones. One of the sisters, for example, could be in Los Angeles, and one could be in London. The boys were born at the same instant, yet the time difference between the two cities was such that their births were on different days.

137. Only one person, the original traveller, is guaranteed to be going to St Ives. Everyone he meets could well be going the other way.

140. The Moon.

141. They were heading away from each other.

143.

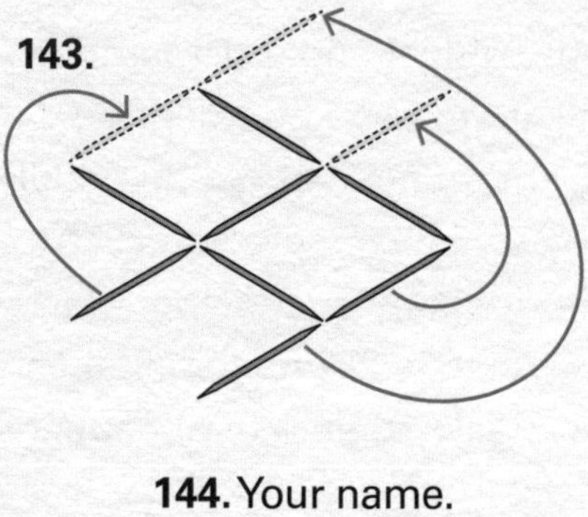

144. Your name.

145. The Sun.

147. 204 – there are 64 single squares, one 8x8 square, four 7x7 squares, nine 6x6 squares, sixteen 5x5 squares, twenty-five 4x4 squares, thirty-six 3x3 squares, forty-nine 2x2 squares.

149. They are facing each other.

152. Doing the sum in their head, most people end up with a total of 5,000, but the correct answer is actually 4,100.

153. Tomorrow.

156. Yes. You stop thinking of places to look once you have found it.

157. Your age.

158. The police officer is his mother.

161. A priest.

162. A hole.

165. The guard had been dreaming, so he was punished for being asleep on duty.

168. A promise.

169. Gloves.

172. A cold.

173. A piece from a jigsaw puzzle.

174. A melted snowman.

175. A breath.

176. Take each other's cars.

180. Warmth – you can easily catch a cold.

181. A stamp.

183.

1	2	20	23	19
3	25	4	12	21
22	18	13	5	7
24	6	11	16	8
15	14	17	9	10

184. There are 11 solutions:

123+45-67+8-9=100; 123+4-5+67-89=100; 123-45-67+89=100;

123-4-5-6-7+8-9=100; 12+3+4+5-6-7+89=100;

12+3-4+5+67+8+9=100;

12-3-4+5-6+7+89=100; 1+23-4+56+7+8+9=100;

1+23-4+5+6+78-9=100;

1+2+34-5+67-8+9=100; 1+2+3-4+5+6+78+9=100

187. A hole.

188. A pillow.

190. Fire.

191. An hourglass.

192. They are back to back.

193. Once. After that you are subtracting 10 from 90 and so on.

194. Six cows and two chickens.

195. His son.

196. One of them was bald.

197.

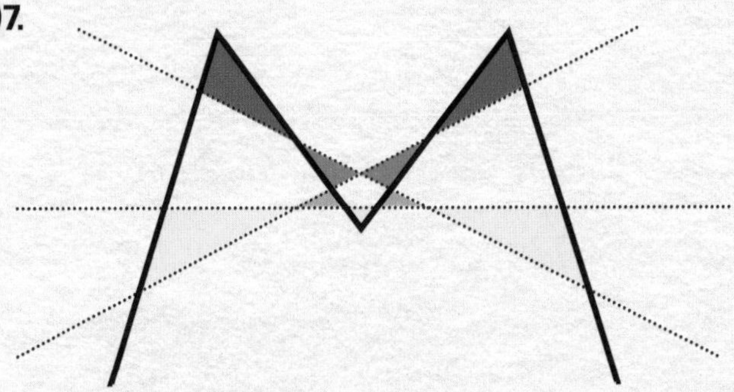

200. 20,000.

201. He was painting the window frames inside the house.

202. He can ask either one of them which way the other one would tell him to go. The liar will point him in the wrong direction. The truth-teller will also point him in the wrong direction, because that's where the liar would tell him to go. So he knows not to take the path that is pointed out for him, but to take the other one.

207. Turn over both hourglasses. Wait until the 7-minute hour glass runs out and then turn it over again. After four minutes, the 11-minute glass will run out, so you must immediately turn the 7-minute glass back again as you know it has four minutes worth of sand in the bottom. When the 7-minute glass is empty, it will have timed four minutes on top of the 11 minutes from the other glass, making a total of 15 minutes.

208. A sponge.

210. 45 – one-fifth of 45 is 9 and 45 plus 9 is 54.

211. The third day after Wednesday is Saturday; therefore, the day after tomorrow is Saturday. That makes today Thursday and the day before yesterday was Tuesday.

213. A game of chess.

214. A computer keyboard.

215. Jane would know she was an eagle if Freddy and Mike both had bear badges. She couldn't tell, therefore Freddy and Mike must either have an eagle and a bear or both have eagles. If Freddy had a bear, then Mike would know he had an eagle, but Mike can't tell. Freddy can be sure, therefore, that he is in the Eagle team.

218. You can't dig half a hole.

219. Lewis Carroll based this riddle on Shakespeare's play *The Merchant of Venice*, where the moneylender Shylock demanded a pound of flesh from his victim if his debt was not paid. The legal judgment went against Shylock when he demanded the pound of flesh because he was allowed to take flesh but no blood. Most people would say that each of the pieces of stick should weigh quarter of a pound, but they would actually weigh less because of the sawdust that was lost when they were cut. Like Shylock overlooking the blood, everyone overlooks the sawdust.

220. Six cows and two chickens.

221. His son.

223. A snail.

224. E N T (they are the first letters of the numbers One to Ten).

227. He throws it up in the air.

228. A clock.

229. Icicles.

230. There were no stairs because it is a bungalow, built on one floor.

232. 20

233.

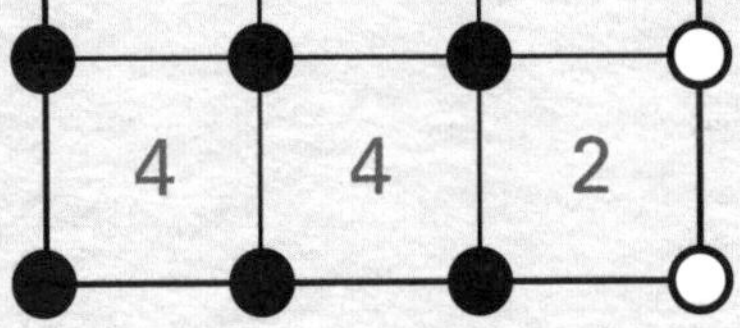

236. Yesterday, today and tomorrow.

237. The only place in the world where the man could run south, west, then north and end up back where he started is at the North Pole. The most likely colour for the bear is, therefore, white, as it would be a polar bear.

240. 888 + 88 + 8 + 8 + 8 = 1,000

241. All seven are girls.

244. A sieve.

245. 3 x 5,694 = 17,082

246. There are four sequences:

192, 384, 576

219, 438, 657

273, 546, 819

327, 654, 981

247. They were grandfather, son and grandson.

249. The man is a priest.

250. A bar of soap.